4·8

D1443748

The World of the Beaver

A LIVING WORLD BOOK
John K. Terres, Editor

LIVING WORLD BOOKS

John K. Terres, Editor

THE WORLD OF THE BEAVER

Text and Photographs by

LEONARD LEE RUE III

J. B. Lippincott Company, Philadelphia & New York

Title page wood engraving by John De Pol

To the world's finest in-laws
Alice and Lew Castner

Contents

Author's Introduction

I BELIEVE ALMOST EVERYONE is interested in beavers. This book has been written with the desire both to stimulate and to satisfy that interest. I can't remember a time when I was not interested in these animals. We are fortunate today in having them to see and to study because this would not have been possible fifty years ago. Beavers are again found in almost all of their original range, and I have studied them over much of it both here in the United States and in Canada.

My thanks go to the many men who have spent countless hours out in the swamps, ponds, and forests studying and reporting their findings about beavers. They are legion, and their work has added to our store of knowledge of this fascinating animal.

I want to thank the many game commissions all over the country that have generously supplied me with so much of their hard-earned data. By using these data along with my personal observations, I hope I have made their job of informing the general public about beavers a little easier.

Three personal friends who have helped me more than I can repay are Lester MacNamara, Leon Kitchen, and Joseph Taylor. May this acknowledgment be testimony of my indebtedness.

Again, John K. Terres, my editor and friend, and I have tried to make this book as enjoyable and knowledgeable as it is within our power to do. Your pleasure will be our reward.

And, if it were not for my wife, Beth, I doubt that this book would have ever been completed. She not only has to decode my writing, she also has to put up with me while I do the writing, a taxing combination. To her I say, "Thank you, dear."

LEONARD LEE RUE III

January, 1964

The World of the Beaver

This excellent beaver study shows its typical body form when on land. Note the highly humped back and flat tail.

The Beaver

OUR MODERN BEAVER is directly descended from the prehistoric Castoroides of a million years ago, the largest rodent ever found on earth. The prehistoric beaver reached fantastic weights of 700 to 800 pounds. The beaver of today is a rarity in the mammal world because he never stops growing nor reaches his maximum growth potential. In the wild, the beaver's life span is about twelve years, although captive specimens have reached the grand old age of nineteen years. The second largest rodent in the world, the beaver is exceeded in size only by the capybara of South America.

The beaver is classified as a rodent because of its dentition consisting of four gnawing incisors or front teeth and sixteen hypsodont rear molars. It is the sole member of the family Castoridae.

In the order of Rodentia the beaver is more closely related to the squirrels and marmots because two of its lower leg bones, like theirs, are separate and not fused together as are those of the mice and rats.

The gnawing teeth of all of the rodents are truly remarkable because they are constantly growing and become sharper with use. The outer front layer is composed of a bright orange enamel, which is very hard, while the rear portion of the tooth is made up of a softer dentine. As the animal gnaws, the dentine wears down much faster than the enamel, giving the tooth a definite chisel-edged shape. The teeth are self sharpening because the lower

15

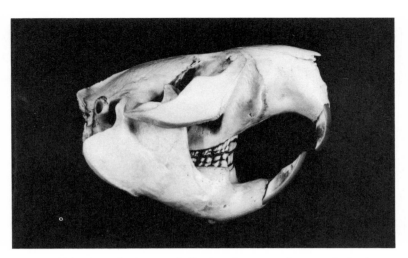

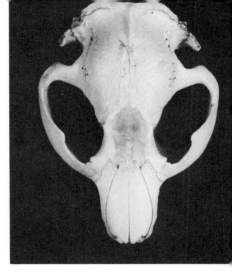

Side view of a beaver skull. Note large gap between the incisors and the molars.

Dorsal view of a beaver skull.

pair works against the upper pair. If, by accident or malformation, the teeth no longer meet, or oppose each other, malocclusion occurs. Then the deformed teeth may grow to 6 or 7 inches in length, forming odd curves or circles. This may prevent the beaver from being able to eat, or the tooth may grow back, piercing the skull. Death results in either case.

One advantage that the beaver enjoys over the other rodents is that its molars, or grinding teeth, very seldom ever show any signs of wear.

The beaver is a semiaquatic mammal whose basic shape and form have been admirably designed to allow it to live under the prevailing conditions of its environment and habitat. Its body design is based upon the simple physical principle that a large body having a small surface area is most efficient for survival under the cold water and icy conditions that are encountered constantly by the beaver.

An average adult will weigh between 40 to 60 pounds and measure about 48 inches in length. Young beavers, of course, weigh less, and there are many records of larger adults weighing much more. In 1960, a Missouri trapper caught a giant that weighed 96 pounds. The record, however, is still held by Vernon Bailey, of the United States Biological Survey, who in August,

16

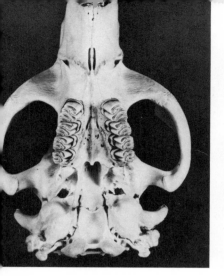

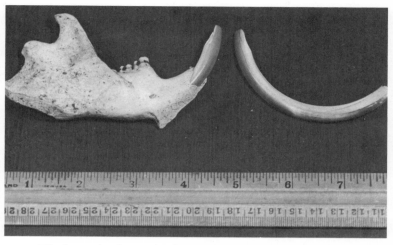

Ventral view of a beaver skull.

The lower jawbone of a beaver and an incisor tooth, showing its great length.

1921, caught a beaver on the Iron River in Wisconsin that weighed 110 pounds.

Perhaps the most outstanding characteristic of the beaver is its large, flattened, paddle-shaped tail. When this appendage can be seen, it rules out any possibility of confusing the beaver with any other species of animal, anywhere in the world. The tail length will measure, in a large specimen, about 16 inches to 17 inches overall. The base of the tail is covered with the same fur as is the body. The flattened portion of the tail, however, measures about 12 inches in length, 6 to 7 inches in width, and has a thickness of about ¾ inch. This part of the tail is covered with scales and some sparse, short, bristly hairs. This scaly tail caused confusion among some of the early explorers, as was recorded by Thomas Jeffreys in 1760. He reported "that the geographer to the King of England had written that the college of Physicians and faculty of Divinity at Paris had given their approval of eating the meat of beaver on fast days because the beaver's scaly tail classified it as a fish and not a mammal." The tail serves as rudder and diving plane for the beaver while swimming. It is seldom used for actual locomotion. The tail also forms a very effective prop when the animal sits upright to feed or is at work at cutting down a tree.

17

Beaver.

When he first comes out of the water,
a beaver is as slick as a greased pig.

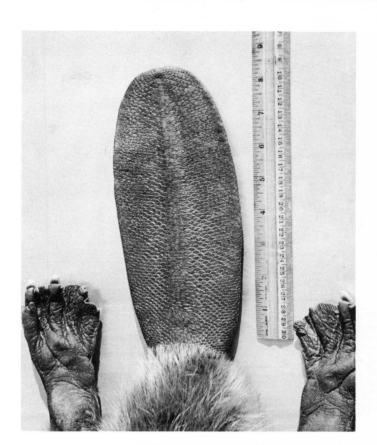

Beaver tail and feet.

Close-up of a beaver's tail. The scales resemble those of a snake, a bird's legs, or a pine cone.

The World of the Beaver

The fur of the body itself is composed of two layers, consisting of long, silky guard hairs and a dense, wooly undercoating. The fur is so thick and usually so well oiled that water almost never wets through to the skin. When the fur is wet, while the animal is swimming, its texture is so smooth and slippery that I can give you no accurate description of it. It has to be felt to be understood. The color of the fur varies from light blond to jet black. Occasionally an albino is found. As a further protection against the cold, the beaver has a subcutaneous layer of fat, which provides excellent insulation. It also makes a beaver one of the most difficult of all animals to skin.

The ears and the nose of the beaver are valvular, allowing both organs to be thoroughly stoppered and protected when the beaver plunges beneath the water's surface. The eyes are protected from the irritation of the water by transparent eyelids that serve as diving goggles, giving the beaver good vision beneath the surface. Water is prevented from going into the beaver's mouth by two folds of skin, one on either side of the mouth, that meet behind the front incisors. They effectively seal off the rest of the mouth and allow the beaver to chew upon wood, either on land or beneath the water, and yet get neither wood splinters nor water into its mouth.

The forepaws of the beaver have five toes with long stout nails, which are effectively used in digging. The paws are very flexible, and the beaver has as much control over them as we do our hands, even though it lacks an opposable thumb. These front feet are not used in swimming, but are carried, balled up like little fists, against the chest.

The hind feet are strong and have five fully webbed toes. The whole foot measures between 6 to 7 inches in length. The beaver's feet have no hair covering at all. The two inside nails on each of the beaver's hind feet have double or split nails, with

A beaver's nostrils are on the sides of its nose, which allows them to be closed more readily underwater.

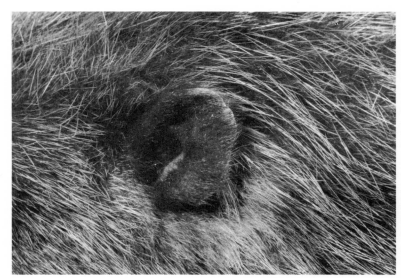

A beaver's ear is valvular so that it can be shut to keep out the water.

Dale

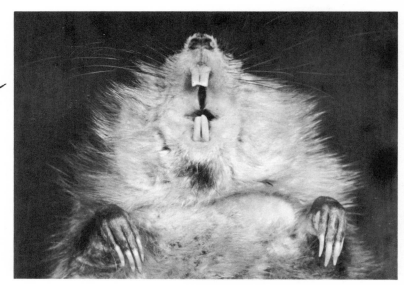

The fur mouth flaps of this muskrat are identical to those of the beaver.

the second nail being exceedingly well developed. These split nails are used as a comb by the beaver when dressing its fur. Beavers spend a great deal of time combing their fur. This takes out any tangles in the fur that would lessen its streamlined effectiveness, as well as removing any ectoparasites, such as body lice or fleas. The beaver has also been observed removing splinters from between its incisors by using this split toenail.

As if the beaver were not unique in enough different ways, it also has a single cloacal opening for all the functions of the scent, reproductive, and excretory organs. It is impossible to tell the sex of a beaver externally unless it is a female during a lactating period. At that time the four nipples of her mammary glands may be seen between her front legs. At other times an internal examination for the male's baculum must be made.

The perineal scent glands, or castors, are two large oblong glands, each with its own duct emptying into the cloaca. The castors lie on either side of the cloaca and measure about 4 inches long and about 5 inches in circumference. They are filled with a rich, thick, deep-yellow, oily liquid. This castoreum is used by the beaver for waterproofing its fur, as well as a means of communication. Castoreum has long been used by man in medicine, and it used to be considered a cure-all for such varied ailments as colic, rheumatism, arthritis, pleurisy and many, many more. Castoreum is still used as a base for expensive perfumes. The basic composition of the oil allows it to retain any fragrance to which it is subjected; yet it will gradually release this fragrance upon being warmed by human body heat. The main use of castoreum today is as a base for animal scents used in trapping. Castoreum is not only attractive to beavers, but has the ability to lure almost all other animals.

The beaver's stomach has a large gland at its upper end, which gives off an enzyme to help reduce woody plant material into food. Research has been done to determine whether the same type of bacteria exists in the beaver's stomach as in the stomach of various ruminants to assist in working on the cellulose that forms the bulk of their diet. I have been unable to find conclusive reports on this matter.

The beaver, being a mammal, is an air-breather, even though it spends perhaps half of its life in the water. Special adaptations permit it to stay submerged for long periods of time. Unless it has been alarmed, a beaver usually submerges about three minutes at a time. The longest time that I have personally recorded is eight minutes forty-four seconds. Edward R. Warren has recorded a beaver as having stayed submerged for fifteen minutes, and other experts have come up with similar timings. It is generally agreed that the beaver can swim submerged for ½ mile or more.

Under similar conditions, most creatures would be adversely affected by the lack of oxygen going to the brain and the buildup of carbon dioxide throughout the body system. The beaver has large lungs and an oversized liver, which allows for the storage of more air and oxygenated blood. The beaver's heartbeat slows down as it dives, so that less oxygen is actually consumed. In addition, there is a constriction of the blood vessels going to the animal's extremities, while the flow of blood to the vital brain area remains normal. This means that the beaver can get much more use out of the supply of blood that it carries. As a further bonus, the animal's respiratory system can tolerate large amounts of carbon dioxide without any complications. And, upon surfacing, the beaver recharges its lungs much more completely than do we humans. A man exchanges about 15 to 20 per cent of the cubic contents of his lungs upon exhaling, while the beaver exchanges 75 per cent or more.

There is some disagreement among authorities about the rating of the degree of development of the beaver's senses. Most

A beaver's forefoot showing the separated toes.

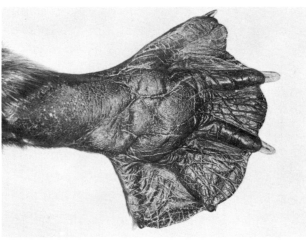

A web of skin connects all of the toes on the beaver's hind feet.

of them rate hearing as the most highly developed. Although the external portion of the beaver's ear is small, the auditory canal is large, and the beaver hears not only airborne sound but vibrations beneath the water and can accurately classify them as being dangerous or otherwise.

I feel that the sense of smell should rank second and base my claim on the fact that when beavers are alarmed by some object that causes them to be suspicious, they will try to swim around the object until their noses can confirm its identity. Many times I have kneeled in my canoe, in the twilight hours, studying beaver. Although I remained motionless, I was in plain sight. If the beavers discovered my presence, they would not dive until they had circled the canoe to pick up my scent. This proves

24

A close-up of the split toenail or "combing" claw on a beaver's hind foot.

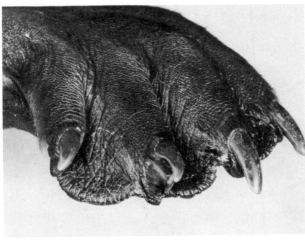

The inner two claws on the beaver's hind feet are split, with the second one being more highly developed.

that although the eyes may discover an object, it takes the final confirmation of the nose to decide action. This I find to be true with almost all mammals. An object has to move to be identified by the eyes. Then again, a beaver upon emerging from the lodge will slowly swim in circles with its head above the water while its ears and nose search for the telltale sound or scent of danger. When it has decided that the way is clear, the beaver will then start to feed, but usually goes out on the bank on the windward side so that if any animal is lurking in the underbrush, its scent will be borne down to the beaver by the wind. Feeding on the leeward side would put the beaver at a distinct disadvantage because it would allow its own body scent to be carried to the enemy, yet effectively conceal the enemy's presence from the beaver.

25

Spring

THE APRIL WIND had shifted during the night and now blew steadily from the south, bringing a warm rain with it. The temperature, which had been hovering below freezing, suddenly soared upward, and the spring thaw was on. The difference in the temperatures of the melting snow and the moist humid air formed a mist that threw a shroud over the forest, seemingly in an effort to conceal the winter's death from all prying eyes. It was a fact, however, that couldn't be hidden. Nature now responded everywhere to the change. Small brooks gathered the runoff water, seemed to gargle their throats, and hurried on down the hill. The streams flexed their muscles and raised the ice that had covered the beaver pond like a mantle.

The beaver lodge, like a large mound of trash and sticks, projected above the ice. Inside, the old female beaver raised up from her sleeping shelf, waddled over to the plunge hole, and dived through and out into the dark waters beyond. Swimming beneath the water directly to the dam, the female saw that the rising water had at last broken the ice free from the mud and stick barrier. Using both her head and her teeth, she soon had enlarged a hole in the ice big enough so that her head could be thrust through. Drinking in the sounds and the scents of the rain-drenched forest was exhilarating after the months of imprisonment by the ice.

26

Spring

This is the first photo of a beaver taken underwater. It shows the hind feet being used in unison while the beaver swims leisurely.

Spring is a time of life, a time of birth. The streams were swollen as they labored to carry away the remains of the winter. The buds on the trees, which had lain dormant since fall, were swollen too. The belly of the female beaver was also swollen as she felt within her the stirrings of a new generation of beavers. And so it was throughout the land, in ponds, in lakes, in streams, that the beaver females were aware of the awakenings and the stirring of the earth and all its creatures.

The breakup of the ice on lakes, ponds, and rivers is usually accomplished in a short time. In the Far North, within a few days of the reappearance of open water, the first ducks come arrowing

27

The World of the Beaver

A beaver alert for danger.

in over the treetops and with set wings drop down to rest and feed. Many have paired on the southern wintering grounds and now are ready for nesting. What is it that tells the ducks, a thousand miles away, that their breeding grounds are suddenly clear? Perhaps they do not "know," but the lengthening days and their recurring breeding cycle bid them to move northward to the breeding grounds at the proper time. In ponds, salamanders and frogs wriggle up out of the mud, not knowing that hibernation has saved them from death by winter starvation or freezing.

Green things thrust up in an effort to establish their own place in the sun. Through some wizardry of chemistry, the

Anxious to supplement its winter's diet of bark, this beaver is searching for newly sprouted green stuff.

skunk cabbage has melted a growing space right up through the solid ice and has a head start over other early spring plants. This fact does not escape the beavers. They are glad to partake of the succulence of spring by feeding upon the young shoots and even digging up the roots.

In April, there are many changes in the beaver family's social structure. The adults have bred in January and February, and the period that a mother beaver carries the young in her body is about 115 to 120 days. Up to this time, the family has consisted of the adult male and female, their offspring of two years ago, and last year's kits. Because a beaver matures slowly, this

29

The World of the Beaver

A two-year-old beaver leaves the lodge.

gives the young an opportunity to develop under the protection and guidance of the parents.

Suddenly this all changes. Now the two-year-olds are driven forcibly from the lodge by the adults. Rebuked and rebuffed, the two-year-olds in bewilderment leave the colony and set forth on their own. Most of them, upon leaving, head *downstream* because most of the beaver dams are located upstream on headwaters. To go upstream would be, for a young beaver, to run into a dead end. Occasionally if a two-year-old refuses to leave, it may be killed. This has happened many times where beavers have been kept in captivity. The underlying cause for this action has a good solid basis. Of greatest importance is that driving the two-year-olds away prevents overpopulation of the colony, which would result in the rapid depletion of the available food; it also reduces the chances of the spread of infectious diseases and prevents inbreeding of the species.

Every beaver colony, from the first day of construction, has a limit to the length of time it can be occupied. This time is regulated by the amount of food available. Beavers do many things to extend their tenancy in the area, such as increasing the height of the dam to raise the water level so that more food is brought within their reach. Additional dams also are built above the main dam for the same purpose, and canals are constructed so that distant food supplies can be moved in. Yet in spite of all this, the time comes when the beavers must move. It is to forestall this day that the two-year-olds are driven out.

As the time of birthing approaches in May, the female usually chases the male from the lodge. The yearling kits may also be driven out of the lodge and forced to take up temporary quarters elsewhere, too. If there is a vacant lodge in the colony, the male and the kits may move into it, or they may live in some of the various auxiliary dens in the banks of ponds and streams, which are a part of most colonies. The male may even leave the colony completely to roam around for awhile, but the yearlings invariably stay in the same pond.

The female at this time is very busy preparing the lodge for the arrival of her young. New bedding is needed, and so she cuts aspen and birch sticks into small lengths and carries them into the lodge. Using her incisors, she splits them into long soft fibers. Grasses cannot be used for bedding because they would get wet while being brought under water to the lodge and they would mat, mold, and rot. The wood strips, on the other hand, allow the water to run through and remain clean, soft, and dry. This

31

The World of the Beaver

is just another example of an animal adapting itself, possibly through thousands of years of evolution, to the best method of solving the problem confronting it.

Beavers have only one litter a year, and this seems to be all that is needed for the species to maintain itself. They reach maturity at two years of age when they are capable of breeding. Based on a rule of thumb that the age at the beginning of breeding maturity is equal to one sixth of a life span, the beaver can expect to live to be about twelve years old. This is undoubtedly about the average age, although there are numerous records of beavers kept in captivity living much longer. Major S. S. Flower of England raised one beaver that lived to be nineteen years old. So far as I can discover, this is the record for beaver longevity. Captive animals usually have longer life spans than do those creatures that must fend for themselves in the wilds. Captive animals are usually longer lived because in captivity they are protected from starvation, accidents, diseases, and natural enemies.

The average litter size is four, but there may be as few as two or as many as seven. One unusual record of ten embryos was recorded by a Mr. R. Brown. The Pennsylvania Game Commission also has records of well-developed embryos numbering seven and nine in two females in early February. This can only be explained by advanced conditions, which brought the breeding season to a successful completion much earlier than is common.

A birthing of a beaver in captivity that was witnessed was reported to have taken sixty-eight to seventy-two hours for six kits to be born. The female sits upright with her tail protruding forward and the cloaca exposed. The baby beavers are each about 15 inches long, counting their tails, and each weighs about 1 pound. Their eyes are open, and they are fully furred. Within an hour, the little ones are nursing. Kits have been seen swimming when they were only thirteen hours old, and they do this without

This colony was abandoned because of a food shortage.

the urging that is needed before some of the other baby water animals will take to the water.

The females have four nipples located between their front legs. The milk is yellowish, rich, and sticky. The young ones nurse for about a month and grow rapidly before they are weaned. Weeks before this, they are following the mother about as she feeds at night, and they are already supplementing their milk diet with various kinds of plant life.

By the time the babies are two weeks old, the yearlings, if they had moved out, will have moved back into the main lodge with the mother. The male, too, may now come back to complete the family unit.

Unless the spring floods do damage to the dam, very little construction work is undertaken, although the condition of the dam is checked by the beavers daily. Both spring and summer are times of comparative ease and relaxation for the beaver. So many people have the erroneous idea that beavers labor mightily and constantly that it has given rise to such phrases as "eager beaver," "work like a beaver," or "he's a beaver for work." The beaver can and does work long and hard when the need arises, but spring and summer are not seasons of labor. The main concerns of beavers at this time are their daily food and caring for their young.

Their food now is mainly grasses, ferns, roots, and almost all kinds of water plants. They may cut down a few trees, but after being on a diet of bark all winter, they understandably seem to prefer a little variety.

No one ever thinks of the beaver as a frolicsome sort of creature. It is more the stoic, solid, burgher type. Its bulky body and short legs are adapted for a more sedate gait, which rules out sudden, frivolous movements. The young, of course, are like young the world over, engaging in games of tag in the water and

An auxiliary beaver dam above the main dam to facilitate food gathering.

Pieces of fine wood shredded by beavers for bedding.

generally scampering around getting in the way. The kits are more vocal than the adults too. Several years ago, I was in a beaver swamp in northern New Jersey just at dawn. The two adults were swimming around my canoe, slapping their tails and diving under the surface, only to reappear a few moments later. As I approached their lodge, I could plainly hear the cries of the kits inside. I imagine that the little ones were crying for food because this period of the day is when the adults are out feeding themselves before retiring for the oncoming daylight hours.

I don't know whether all the tail slapping that the adults

36

Royal ferns cut and fed upon by beavers.

were doing was an attempt to scare me away from the lodge, or whether it was done as a warning to the young to be silent, but it failed in both cases. This slapping of the tail on the water is perhaps one of the most widely known of all beaver characteristics. It is virtually impossible to be in, or to travel through, beaver country without witnessing it. Much has been written on this trait, and many studies have been made concerning it. It is generally agreed that the explosive crack and the splashing of the water is an alarm signal. The sound travels well and for long distances over the water. I have heard beavers close by that I had alarmed slap the water as they dived, and then heard others in the distance slap the water too as they passed the danger signal along. I had not alarmed the more distant beavers, but when one signals, quite frequently others will too.

In addition to signaling other beavers, I believe that the water slapping is also done to startle or confuse a nearby enemy. One naturalist writes of a beaver approaching his swimming dog that slapped the water repeatedly so that the dog turned away rather than face the splashing water. In shallow water, I have seen beavers that were cornered splash with their tails, showering everything with a deluge of mud and water. In this confusion, the beaver often made good its escape. I have also seen beavers on dry land, when alarmed, slap their tails against the ground, so deeply ingrained is this slapping habit.

Most of the beavers in an area will respond to this warning signal most of the time, but there are exceptions. Quite frequently the babies will not react to the signal, and there are times when adults won't either. Sometimes the adults want to ascertain the danger for themselves before being alarmed. A beaver in deep water is less apt to be alarmed by the warning signal because it is already in a place of safety. Beavers feeding or resting in the shallows will slip into the water and swim out to a greater depth, while those up on the land will hurry to the water and dive in, usually slapping their tails, too.

Lloyd Tevis, studying a beaver colony in the Edmund Niles Huyck Preserve at Rensselaerville, New York, has reported that there were only thirteen active responses to twenty-one warning dives that he witnessed. The findings of others seem to bear out this ratio. That the kits would be the least likely to respond to the alarm signal is logical. Although most creatures exhibit instinctive behavior patterns, there is also much they must learn, either from teaching or experience.

The water flies as the beaver slaps the danger signal.

The great French anatomist Baron Cuvier (1769-1832) very ably proved that almost all of the beaver's actions are instinctive. To do this, he isolated several baby beavers completely from all contact with any other beaver. The young beavers were even breast fed on human milk. When the beavers grew up, they exhibited all the talents and accomplishments of beavers that had been reared naturally by their parents in the wild. It is questionable if these land-reared beavers would have been able to survive if released in the wilds. The knowledge of danger usually has to

The otter is the
beaver's greatest
natural enemy.

This beaver is in
shallow water, which
accounts for the fur
on his back being
dry.

40

Timber wolves prey upon any beaver they can catch upon land.

This conspicuous plunge hole was about fifty feet from the bank of the stream.

41

be taught, and these beavers probably would have been killed before they learned to recognize all the dangers that a mother would have taught them.

Because of their body size and their way of life, beavers are not subject to the predation that befalls most of the smaller creatures. The stout lodge with its underwater entrances is a superb defense against most of the land animals. The otter is the beaver's main enemy. It, too, is a water animal, and more at home there (where it can outswim a trout) than it is on land. Underwater entrances of beavers are no barriers to it. The otter can outswim and, being a meat-eater, can outfight the average beaver. A large beaver may prove too tough an adversary for an otter, but a beaver kit may afford an otter a tasty meal.

The beaver is exposed to the greatest danger when it leaves the water to forage for food. On land, wolves, coyotes, lynxes, bobcats, mountain lions, wolverines, bears, and even stray dogs, depending upon the section of the country, may catch and kill a beaver. This is not the easy task it may appear because the beaver is a plucky fighter when it needs to be. Its weight is an advantage, its hide is tough, its body fat a protection, and its powerful front teeth are formidable weapons of defense. Beavers fighting for their lives have been known to bite their attackers and drag them underwater to drown.

In addition to the larger predators, the kits are subject to attack by foxes, martens, fish, hawks, owls, and some baby beavers have probably been gobbled up by the big great northern pike. Man, as with all wildlife, is the beaver's greatest enemy.

One aspect of defense, or escape, that is seldom noted is the beaver's use of plunge holes. These are made by the beaver in digging long tunnels under the earth that are filled, or partially filled, with water. One entrance to such a tunnel is underwater, the other on land. The plunge holes themselves are dug upward through the forest floor and are well hidden and seldom used so that the vegetation usually covers the hole from sight. Some of them are 30 to 40 feet from the water's edge. They are used exactly like the hidden plunge holes dug by most of the ground-dwelling rodents. It is very easy to see what an asset they must be to beavers in a time of danger when some predator has slipped between the beaver and the pond's edge in an effort to cut it off from water.

I have usually discovered these holes by stepping in them or falling through the roof of the tunnel. For many years, I have examined and photographed every beaver colony that I came upon. In the course of these examinations, I discovered the plunge holes. Almost every beaver colony that I have found in Canada usually has these escape tunnels, while most of the colonies in the United States do not. The only reason I can advance for this is that the Canadian colonies that I checked were in virgin forests where the fallen trees and the accumulated trash of centuries made a veritable "giant's jackstraws." In the United States, most of the beaver-colony areas are a little more open, having less restrictive underbrush, so that even a bulky beaver can perhaps escape by running on top of the ground to reach the water. Even so, occasional plunge holes may be found here.

Swimming is one means of escape from danger for the beaver. Swimming is also one of its means of locomotion, one of the easiest ways of transporting its body bulk, and a means of securing food. In short, swimming to a beaver is its way of life. Is it any wonder then that the beaver is so adept at it?

When the beaver dives below the surface, its nose and ear valves close automatically. The transparent eyelids slide across the eyes allowing excellent vision beneath the water without the prospect of getting irritants in the eye or having the eye fluids washed away. These eyelids also act as a pair of safety goggles to

This photo of a beaver swimming completely underwater shows the feet being used in alternate stroking, with the far foot going back as the near foot is moved forward.

Rear view of a beaver swimming underwater, showing the great extension of the toes and web of the hind feet for propulsion.

44

This underwater view of a beaver swimming on the surface shows that, like an iceberg, nine-tenths of his body is beneath the surface. Note that the rear feet are being used alternately.

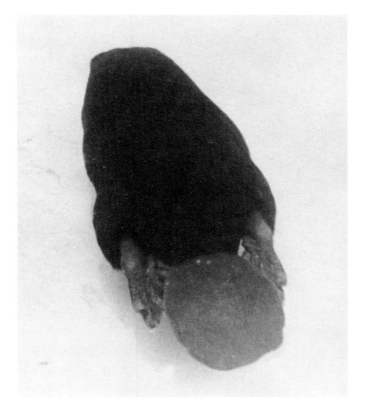

Top-rear view of a large beaver showing both feet being used at one time.

A beaver swimming at the usual rate of about two miles an hour.

prevent sticks and wood chips from damaging the eye. I honestly believe that the beaver's vision is better underwater than it is on the surface.

The beaver's forepaws are not webbed, and therefore are not used for propulsion in swimming. It has been recorded that the beaver allows the forepaws to merely hang down against its lower chest while swimming. Actually the feet are balled up into little fists and carried high against the chest, where they serve exactly as do the bumpers on our automobiles. When the beaver swims through underwater brush or tangles, the forefeet are used to fend off the branches and sticks that would obstruct passage. In surfacing, the beaver invariably brings its forepaws up with out-stretched toes to prevent collision with any object that may be floating on the water's surface. In carrying loads of mud or debris, to be used on the lodge or dam, the beaver carries the burden between its chin and chest and holds it against its chest with the top of its front feet. Sticks are usually carried in the mouth and held by the incisors.

The back feet of the beaver are the main source of swimming power. The wide-spreading toes are connected with a very flexible web of skin. As the beaver recovers from a stroke, the toes are brought together and bent inward and the foot is lifted upward to the body, which reduces drag to a minimum. As the stroke is started, the toes are spread apart, straightened, and the foot moves down and out. This allows for tremendous pressure to be brought to bear on the water and propels the beaver forward at a good rate of speed.

There is quite a bit of discussion on just how a beaver uses its feet in swimming. Some people claim the beaver makes its strokes in unison, with both feet going back together. Others claim that it uses them in an alternate fashion. They are both correct because the beaver uses *both* methods, but for different purposes. When

47

the beaver is swimming underwater or on the surface at a leisurely rate, it uses its feet in unison. But let it be alarmed or really want to get some place in a hurry, and it will use the alternate stroking.

Most of the underwater swimming is done with the feet in unison because the beaver is actually coasting most of the time when it is underwater. It makes a powerful double stroke and then glides with its rear feet trailing out behind. If it were to glide trying to use the alternate stroke, one foot would always be advanced, producing considerable drag.

How do I know just what the beaver does in swimming underwater? That's easy, because I have been there. I have spent considerable time swimming underwater with beavers, watching and photographing them while I used both snorkels and aqualungs. It was by this method that I was able to disprove the current belief that a beaver swims at a rate of 2 miles per hour. Whoever wrote that has never gone underwater and grabbed a beaver by the tail. On occasions when I have done just that, the beaver swam so hard that when it hit the surface, over two thirds of its body length would actually shoot right out of the water. Even using gigantic racing fins on my feet, I can't begin to catch up with a beaver swimming. From measured distances and timings, I would say that the beaver can swim on the surface at speeds of at least 5 miles per hour, and when hard pressed can do much better.

The tail also plays a very important part in swimming. Its main use is as a steering device, although on occasion the beaver will flap its tail up and down while underwater to increase speed. The tail is a very effective diving plane and allows the beaver good maneuverability when flexed in the proper position. When the beaver is towing a leafy branch, the tail is angled in the opposite direction to overcome the turning pull of the dragged branch. Without the control provided by its tail, the beaver would be forced to swim in circles because of the drag of the branch.

Notice the waves thrown up by a beaver swimming at its top speed of about six miles an hour.

49

The World of the Beaver

A very interesting ritual to watch is the care and dressing of its fur that the beaver engages in immediately upon leaving the water. Waddling ashore, it sits upright, then, using its forepaws, carefully shakes the water out of its ears. A few leisurely scratches of the hair on its head, and then, perhaps, it rubs its eyes and combs its whiskers. Stretching itself upright, it then indulges in some good healthy belly scratching. This luxury accomplished, it then begins to comb its fur, using the split toenails on the hind feet. If time is of no importance, this may take five minutes or more as it does the job thoroughly and completely, first on one side and then on the other. After all the preliminaries are taken care of, it oils its fur.

The beaver may or may not have been sitting on its tail to do the cleaning job, but it must do so to oil its fur. This is accomplished by raising one hind leg and sweeping its tail under its body, or the beaver simply bends the tail down, backs up, and ends up sitting on it. By sitting on its tail, the beaver exposes the cloaca and the oil glands it contains. Reaching down with its forefeet, the beaver get the oil on its paws and then proceeds to transfer the oil to its fur. This may take another five minutes, but at completion its coat is considered the ultimate in sartorial splendor.

Summer

A BEAVER POND in the summer seems almost to boil with activity. Many kinds of insects hatch in or near the sunlit waters, and all play an important part in the ecology of the pond. Over in some warm, quiet, backwater area, mosquitoes may find an ideal spot to lay their eggs. At the surface of the water, the "wrigglers," or immature mosquitoes that rise to breathe, are eaten by small fishes, and those mosquitoes that become adults and fly are swept out of the air by the dragonflies that are one of the important checks on the mosquito population. The dragonflies are among the most brilliantly colored of all insects, and they look like shimmering strands of silk as they dart through the air in pursuit of their prey.

The frog that sits silent in the shallows along the shore is waiting for a flying insect or any small water animal to come within range of its quick leap and wide mouth. Tree swallows inscribe graceful arcs in the sky. They, too, gather insects, with which to gorge the young swallows that have been hatched in holes in dead trees standing in the pond waters. By the middle of August, though the sun still stands high in the sky and shines with great warmth, the swallows leave the northern ponds and start southward for their wintering grounds.

During the middle of a warm summer day, few fish are feeding, but the many swirls in the water at dusk show where the trout are concentrating their efforts on the latest hatch of insects.

51

A beaver giving his head a thorough scratching.

The mother wood duck and her accompanying flotilla of young dash and splash as they noisily slurp their protein-rich meals of insects. If you are cautious in your approach to the pond, perhaps you will see the beavers themselves as they laze around in the sun.

When the first explorers came to this country, they wrote of how the beaver worked by day and slept by night, as any good artisan should. The white man changed all that. To secure some measure of protection, beavers changed their habits and began to venture forth only under the protective cover of darkness. However, even today in areas where they are relatively unmolested, they still like to come out and bask in the bright sunshine. I have watched them when they did not know that their sunbathing activities were being observed. They were a study in relaxation,

52

Using his special split toenails, this beaver combs his fur.

and would lie on their stomachs with their feet folded back and their chins outstretched. After a time, they would roll over on their backs with their legs flopping outward like a beat-up rag doll's. About half an hour is all of this luxury they would allow themselves, not because of the press of time, but because their feet and tails dry out very rapidly and may crack. It has been discovered that in order to transplant a beaver successfully from one area to another, great care must be taken that its feet and tail are wet occasionally to prevent them from cracking.

In any event, all beavers become active around sundown. In Quebec, Canada, where I have spent the last fourteen summers, guiding wilderness canoe trips, I have found that you can almost set your watch at 8:30 P.M. at the time when the beavers start to

53

A beaver pond and lodge in the Grand Tetons in Wyoming.

54

leave their lodges. Many times I have surrounded the beaver lodges with a fleet of canoes so that all of the boys in camp could see them as they came out. I have noticed that it is usually the yearlings that leave the lodge first, and they always seem much more anxious to start the night's activities. Perhaps they have not yet learned to have the patience needed by animals to survive in the wilderness.

The young beavers come out of the lodge without much of a disturbance because their small bodies do not displace too much water. When they pop to the surface, it is usually within a few feet of the lodge, and they swim slowly back and forth. Beavers usually void their body wastes as soon as they leave the lodge. They never soil the lodge itself, and I have never seen their excrement on land. Usually their feces can be seen on the bottom of the pond in shallow water and particularly around the lodge itself. If the beavers are not alarmed, several of the young ones may play for a few minutes by chasing, or following, one another around, as if in a game. Then one by one, they swim away, usually in different directions.

There is no doubt in any observer's mind when the adults leave the lodge. They usually come out like a torpedo from its firing tube after the captain shouts, "Fire one!" There is usually a great disturbance and displacement of water accompanied by many bubbles. The water will push away from the lodge, and then surge back from shore with enough turbulence to rock a canoe gently. The adults, upon surfacing, will test the air for danger and if they discover human observers will splash and dive at once. They do not return to the lodge, but will seek safety by swimming underwater for a long distance. Beavers have been known to swim submerged for more than ½ mile.

In the gathering dusk, it is very seldom that we can see one of the adults surface again. If we are not out on the pond, but near the shore, the beavers may not discover us and may swim on about their business. It is seldom that all beavers on emerging from the lodge have the same destination, except for the mother beaver and her kits.

The sound of cutting and chewing can often be heard because sound travels so well over the water. After an hour or more, the beavers usually return to the lodge, often looking like small tug-boats with a payload as they drag in a branch to be used as a midnight snack.

The main food of the beaver in summer depends upon where it lives, since the kinds of plant food vary according to the region. The list will include sedges, berries, flags, or irises, spatterdocks, grasses, wild roses, mushrooms, water lilies, cow parsnips, rushes, burweeds, duckweeds, and the blossoms, leaves, stems, and roots of almost all kinds of water plants. The beaver is a strict vegetarian, and I can find no record of his ever eating meat. If the beaver is living in a farming or gardening area, it will eat carrots, potatoes, rutabagas, turnips, corn, apples, alfalfa, and clover. In agricultural areas, it often gets into trouble by girdling or cutting down fruit trees and decorative willows. However, I was amazed when I first saw a beaver eat alga, or green pond scum. I later found they seek this out whenever possible. They pull in great swaths of it and in consuming it, look as though they are eating green spaghetti. The algae are a rich source of protein and a very nutritious food.

Many people credit the beaver with more sagacity than this remarkable creature actually has. They claim that it can fell a tree in any desired direction. This of course is not true, as can readily be determined by anyone who will take the trouble to investigate it. According to my observations, I find that one out of every five trees that a beaver cuts cannot be used by the beaver because it becomes lodged against other standing trees and never falls to the ground, or else it falls over the tops of other trees already down

A beaver feeding on green algae, or "pond scum."

Showing the extensive cuttings of beavers. Note hung-up tree.

A yearling beaver cutting the bark off an aspen tree at 11:30 P.M.

It often takes more than one cut to fell a tree.

The yearling beaver is stripping off aspen bark to eat before felling the tree.

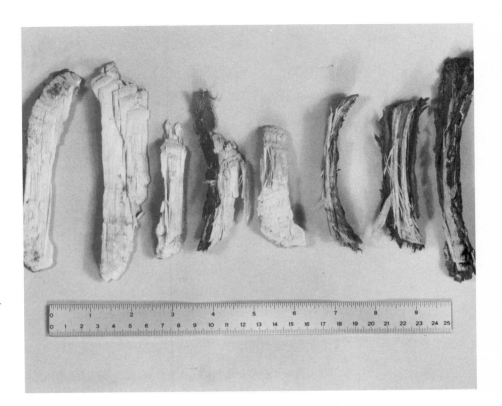

Various-sized chips of wood torn out by a beaver in its cutting.

The larger the diameter of the tree, the larger the chips.

The World of the Beaver

and cannot be reached by the beaver. Most of the trees do fall in the water where beavers want them to, but that is because of good biological reasons and gravity, and not as the direct result of expert woodsmanship. Trees growing along streams will send out many branches on the side toward the stream where there is more sunlight. When such trees are cut, they are heavier on the stream side and fall in that direction, a fact for which the beaver gets all the credit.

Walk back into the woods away from the water's edge where the trees are growing tall and straight and see which way they are felled by beavers. The direction is then determined by such factors as a gust of wind and the cuts in the tree made by the beaver. Wind is such a big factor that beavers do not like to cut trees when a strong wind is blowing steadily. It may send the tree crashing down before the animals are ready.

When a tree becomes hung up in another, the beaver does not know enough to cut the supporting tree, but may make repeated cuts on the hung-up tree itself. If the angle of the hung-up tree is not too steep, the beaver may climb up the inclined trunk in order to cut through it higher up. The animal is not a good climber. However, there is one instance of a beaver having climbed a standing tree, but it is the only one to my knowledge. This beaver climbed up a straight birch tree to a height of about 20 feet above the ground. Ordinarily you can keep a beaver in an open-top wire pen without the risk that it will climb out. A beaver's body is not built for climbing.

When a beaver is felling a tree, it usually stands erect before the tree and braces its tail against the ground. Its tail and hind legs make a very effective tripod, and its forelegs either grasp the tree or just rest against it. A beaver does not hold its head in a normal, upright manner when cutting a tree. Instead, the head is turned sidewards so that the grooves cut by the teeth run in the same direction as would those made by a saw used in felling the tree. The span of the cut, from top to bottom, is determined by the diameter of the tree. The beaver takes several bites at the top of the cut, then takes several bites at the bottom. The chip is then torn out and dropped. Many people believe that the chip is cut out entirely, but this is not so. By examining the chips themselves, you can see where the center fibers have been torn apart and that the only cutting marks are on the end of the chip. Most of the cutting is done by the upper incisors while the lower incisors are held steady, unlike a pair of scissors where both edges cut through to the middle.

As the work progresses toward the center, the chips become smaller. Chips from a hardwood tree are smaller than those cut from a softer tree. There is no set pattern for the actual cutting either. Some trees are cut through entirely from one side, although the usual cutting is done all the way around. Some cuts, for no discernible reason, won't even meet, being high on one side of the tree and low on the other. Some trees will have several cuts all the way around on the one trunk. Sometimes the configuration of the ground around the tree will determine the side to be cut, and at other times some obstruction will force the cutting to be done from just one side. Some trees have had as many as four or five cuts on the one trunk, which resembled a gigantic string of beads. Some of the cuts were so high that they had to be made by the beaver standing on the top of drifted snow.

Often, trees will be cut almost through and then abandoned. My only explanation for this is that something may have frightened the beaver away from the job before it was completed. Sometimes the tree will be cut down the following night, although I have found so many left standing like this that I am led to believe that after they are abandoned they are forgotten. One writer claimed that the beaver would cut a number of trees in this fashion and

This tree has been twice started and twice abandoned.

then wait for a strong wind to knock them down for him. Strong winds sometimes do drop such trees, but not because the beavers had planned it that way.

Usually one beaver will do all of the felling of the tree by itself. On rare occasions two beavers may work together. Old woodcuts showing families of beavers working at cutting down a single tree were the figments of very active imaginations. It would increase the danger to the beavers themselves to have more than one working on a single tree. As it is, an occasional accident will occur where the beaver will be killed by the tree it is felling.

Periodically, photographs are published of beavers that have

62

Occasionally a beaver is killed by the tree he is felling.

been killed while felling trees. Quite frequently the tree falls and pins the foot or the tail of the beaver against the ground. The trapped beaver expends a great deal of energy trying to free itself, as is evidenced by the torn earth and the cutting of everything within reach. There is no record of a trapped beaver being aided by others of the colony. The beaver seldom frees itself and usually dies a lingering death of thirst and starvation. The only trapped beaver that I ever found was much more fortunate because the tree had fallen across its back and had probably killed it instantly.

Under ordinary circumstances, the beaver cuts until the tree starts to fall. The breaking of the remaining fibers of the tree

63

are readily felt in its teeth, and thus warned, it makes a dash for safety, plunging into the water if it is near. Since the crashing of the tree can be heard for a long distance in the still of the night, the beaver usually waits to listen for any predator that may have been attracted by the sound. When everything seems to be all right, the beaver goes ashore, and now the whole family will join in to feed and cut up the branches.

Beavers are very sociable when feeding, and it is very seldom that there is any fuss over food. The beaver kits in particular feed upon any branch or twig that they can reach. If they cannot reach anything, they wait until one of the larger beavers cuts the food down, then they move in to share it and no objections are raised. To me, they are raised like Eskimo children, with indulged tolerance. Even the big beavers share their food, often giving up a branch that they have cut for themselves. I have seen one swim in towing a branch behind it that it had brought along as food; yet when it sat along the shore and prepared to eat, another beaver would join it, and many times the first beaver would leave the branch and swim away to get another for itself. This amiableness is undoubtedly the result of beavers having little competition for food. Of all wild creatures, they probably suffer less from food shortages than any other. Because of this they live a truly communistic type of life.

Armed with chisel-sharp incisors and powerful jaw muscles, the beaver cuts rapidly, particularly in the softer woods. It can down a 5-inch-diameter willow in three minutes, and a 6-inch-diameter birch in about ten minutes. Alders and smaller bushes are dropped off with about eight to ten bites. Some of the trees felled by beavers, however, are real undertakings. The largest tree that I have personally seen them cut was a 34-inch-diameter birch felled on the Doré River in Quebec, Canada. This, however, was dwarfed by a record cottonwood tree that was 37 inches in

A beaver swimming with ears erect for sounds of danger.

Smaller twigs are not peeled but eaten entirely.

65

diameter and 110 feet high, felled by beavers in British Columbia.

We may wonder about the travels of beavers during the summer, especially the two-year-olds that were forced out of the colony in the spring. They have been traveling about, seeking both a mate and a new home. There is usually a higher percentage of males than females, and though there are "bachelor" beavers, there is little likelihood of there ever being any spinsters. Beavers are usually monogamous, and each retains a lifelong association with its mate. The social life of the colony is a matriarchy, dominated by the female. All life revolves around her, and if the adult female is killed, the colony will probably break up. In contrast, if the adult male is killed, another male will probably come along and replace him.

The travels of beavers have been recorded simply by "ear tagging." Although the distances vary, one two-year-old in Minnesota traveled 51 miles in one season; another two-year-old in North Dakota went 148 "stream miles" in seven months. Another record is of 135 miles, but it took this fellow eight years to do it. Beavers may hesitate to travel overland to reach water because it leaves them vulnerable to their enemies; yet there are many records of their doing so. On the mountain behind my northern New Jersey home, beavers were released in one stream, after which they crossed a mountain ridge and traveled about a mile to establish themselves in Sunfish Pond. Water is magnetic to them. They can probably smell it for great distances, and they "home" to it with remarkable accuracy.

As the young beavers travel about, they leave their "calling cards" in the form of mud patties that they saturate with their scent. All beavers establish scent "signposts," but the majority of these mud patties are the work of unmated beavers. To establish a mud patty, a beaver dredges mud up from the bottom of the stream or pond and deposits it upon some outcropping of land or other conspicuous spot. Sometimes the mud will be piled on a fallen log at the water's edge, but usually it will simply be coned up. Frequently grasses will be mixed with the mud. When the beaver is satisfied with its handiwork, it deposits its musk, or castoreum, on the top of it. This strong, pleasing odor soon permeates the entire area and can be smelled for great distances. Our human sense of smell is poor compared to that of a wild animal, but I can locate almost every patty on the shore, even though it may be hidden from sight as I paddle by. Because I recognize the odor and am familiar with it, I can find it; yet boys to whom I have shown the patty may actually have to get their noses right down to the mud before they can smell it. Other beavers, of course, and all other animals quickly locate the castoreum.

A large ash cut by a beaver.

67

The World of the Beaver

These mud patties are similar to the scent posts that most animals, particularly the canine family, use as a means of communication. Each scent post acts as a bulletin board and tells the other animals how long ago the scent was deposited, what was the sex of the maker, what types of food the maker had eaten, and many other things that we humans can only guess at.

If several young males locate a young female at the same time, I don't know by what means she chooses between them. That she will show a marked preference for one particular male has been shown many times by beavers kept in captivity. The males may fight for the favors of the female, but this is not too often the case. Beavers are peaceful, sociable creatures and not given to a great deal of fighting. Unlike muskrats, the skins of beavers

A mud-topped beaver castor patty.

are seldom scarred and cut from fighting. There is little opportunity for fighting in the breeding season in January and February because at that time most of the beavers are securely locked in their own private ponds and have little chance for quarrelsome competition. After a mate has been chosen, the pair will then usually leave the larger stream and start to investigate some of the smaller tributaries seeking out a homesite. Most of their traveling will be done at night for greater protection. Without having the protection of a lodge, they will sleep in the most protected spot they can find. A dense alder thicket makes a good spot, particularly if it is on a small island or on a jutting spit of land. Overhanging banks or fallen trees that are near the water are also favored by them. An abandoned beaver lodge or an old den in the bank of a stream or pond will be used whenever the opportunity presents itself. If they find an old lodge and dam, abandoned years before because of a food shortage, the trees and thickets of the area may have regrown sufficiently to again supply the needed food. If so, the pair may set up housekeeping. If a suitable new damsite cannot be found, or there just is not enough food in the area, the pair may retrace their route and try another stream. Thus they will continue their search until they find, what to them are, ideal conditions.

When a location is favorable for establishing a new colony, the young pair will then spend two or three days checking it thoroughly before choosing the actual damsite. Although beavers are famous as engineers, their skills are often overrated. Their persistence is often just as important in getting the dam built, and in keeping it in shape, as is its actual location. Beavers are like people in that some are much more intelligent than others. Many of the dams of beavers have been washed away or broken, yet few people realize this. Often, by merely choosing a slightly different location for the dam, up or down the stream, only a fraction of the work that was expended by beavers would have been needed. They often construct dams that are 100 feet long, whereas if they had sought the ideal spot they could have held the same amount of water with a dam 25 feet long. Yet, once the beavers start to build, no other spot will do. By sheer hard work, they overcome all the obstacles that are presented. Also, there may be reasons why beavers build where they do that are obscure to a human being.

Dam building is actually a compulsion with beavers. If they decide to build their lodge in a manmade pond, where the water is already held back by a good solid concrete dam, they may still not be satisfied until they try to improve upon the job by attempting to cover the concrete with sticks and mud. When building in large natural lakes, beavers will forego the dam-building urge; however, they will dam the outlet streams of smaller lakes. Quite frequently, in Quebec, where most of the country is very flat, beavers will build their lodges on the long spits of land that are usually formed at each lake's entrance by sediment dropped as the flow of water slows down.

Constant persecution of beavers will cause them to completely abandon dam building. Originally the beavers of Europe built dams and lodges like those of the American beavers. Because of steady harassments and pressures by people they gradually stopped building dams, possibly to escape detection. Gradually they stopped building lodges, too, and reverted to living in dens in the banks of ponds and streams. Little by little, European beavers were eliminated. Finally, and just in time, they were given protection, and their numbers started to increase. At the same time, they began to build dams and lodges again, which proved that the age-old habits had not been lost, but were simply repressed.

When the damsite has finally been selected, the newly paired beavers set to work. They fell shrubs and saplings, and though larger pieces are used later, the bulk of the dam will be con-

The grass growing on this dam shows that the site has been abandoned by beavers.

structed of relatively small material. Alder, which usually grows in dense thickets by streamsides, is the most frequently used wood. Each piece is dragged to the damsite as soon as it is cut and is placed with the butt end facing upstream. The beavers work feverishly because until there is a pool of water into which they can retreat for safety, they are quite vulnerable to lynxes, wolves, and other predatory animals. Almost everything goes into a dam that the beavers can find—live wood, dead wood, mud, grasses, rocks, and, occasionally, even old railroad ties. A fairly substantial dam can be built by a pair of beavers in three or four nights.

71

A dam so newly constructed that the branches still bear leaves.

One time, when beavers were building a dam that was flooding out a railroad culvert, officials of the company sent in a work crew to destroy the dam. In doing so, the men used a 9-foot-long iron poker to help pull the dam apart. When the crew departed for the night, they left the poker lying on the dam. On returning the next morning, the men discovered that the beavers had buried the poker in the dam, which helped to reinforce it.

Many times, when beavers have caused economic damage because of the location of their dams, men have tried to discourage their repair work at night by placing lighted lanterns or flare pots

Note the rocks that have been used in the construction of this dam.

on top of the dam. Almost invariably, when they returned in the morning, they found that the lantern or the flare had been buried by the beavers in the dam itself. In fact, one of the men I talked with was convinced that the beavers enjoyed having the light and that it helped them to see better so they could complete their repair work before daybreak and thus keep ahead of the destruction by the work crews.

In building the dam, beavers raise the crest of it uniformly. Wherever a low spot develops, they place more materials and thereby gradually raise the height evenly. This also allows them to

73

Leon Kitchen, a New Jersey state trapper, setting a live trap on a dam that the beavers built right across a utility road.

extend the wings of the dam as needed. If they built the dam in sections, much effort would be wasted because they would have no way of building it on the same level throughout. They have no levels as carpenters and builders do for guiding their work; therefore they use the waterline, which makes a perfect level.

At first the dam leaks badly, but the beavers soon overcome this. They dredge up mud from the bottom of the pond and plaster it on the dam's upstream side. The flow of the water downstream washes the mud in among the sticks, gradually clogging up the leaks. It is because of this dredging that the deepest part of

Close-up of the material used in an extended wing of a beaver's dam.

a beaver's pond is usually directly below the dam. Rocks are used by them to compress and to weight down the brush in the dam. Some of the stones used by beavers in building their dams weigh as much as 30 to 40 pounds and require a tremendous amount of energy from the animals to put them in place.

Sediment and leaves washed downstream gradually collect against the upstream face of the dam, effectively sealing it shut. A dam in good repair will lose very little water through seepage. A beaver dam is built on good engineering principles, with the base always much wider than the top, which counteracts the

75

Grasping the stick in his teeth,
the beaver pushes it into the
dam to start repairs.

This adult is pulling a stick
up on the dam to repair a break.

The dam repair goes fast
as this beaver brings in
two sticks at a time.

Using both his paws
and his teeth, this big beaver
shoves a branch into the dam.

greater pressures on the bottom of the dam. The upstream face of the dam is not steep, but is tapered upstream like a wedge. Beavers usually take advantage of any boulders, trees, or other natural obstructions that are already in the stream and make them a part of the dam. Because of this, some dams may actually be built "zigzag" across the stream and may look like a *W,* or have some other odd conformation.

Usually, on streams that are fairly open and deep, the dam will be bowed slightly *downstream.* This happens because the water is forcing the material downstream, and the beaver anchors it where it is. On very fast moving streams, particularly in the western United States where the water builds up great pressure rushing down from high altitudes, the beavers will deliberately bow the dam upstream to counteract it.

In a narrow stream bed, the dam may be comparatively short. In wide, flat meadowlands the dams may be hundreds of feet long. The longest dam I have ever seen was about 800 feet long, while another was 177 good paces (about 500 feet long), or as good a pace as I could make while walking along the crest of the dam. The tallest dam I have seen was 8 feet high from the top of the water on the downstream side to the top of the dam. It would have been even higher if I had measured it from the bottom of the stream itself.

The highest beaver dam that I can find records of was one on Taylor's Creek in Bayfield County, Wisconsin, measured in 1919. It was 12 feet high and 640 feet long. Grasse and Putnam, in their studies of beavers in Wyoming in 1955, photographed a dam that was only 30 feet wide but was 18 feet high. A dam on the Jefferson River near Three Forks, Montana, was 2,140 feet long, but the record must go to a dam built by beavers in New Hampshire near the present town of Berlin. It was 4,000 feet long and created a lake containing forty beaver lodges.

Low water has exposed even the base of the downstream side of this dam.

A beaver dam under construction. Note how the shape of the dam is being determined by the existing boulders in the stream.

This dam has a definite bend upstream to counteract the pressure of the fast-moving water.

I'm not sure just what the beavers were trying to accomplish with this dam that was over 800 feet long.

A Canadian beaver dam 500 feet in length.

This dam is composed of alders.

Summer

The width of the top, or crest, of the dam itself, varies in thickness. Sometimes it is only a few inches or so wide, or it may be 3 or 4 feet. The older the dam and the wider the crest, the more solidly packed the whole mass becomes. Often, the crest will be so narrow that you actually stand in water as you try to walk along the top because the crest sinks at each footstep. At other times, an old dam becomes a main bridge over a stream, used by all kinds of wild animals. Even moose will sometimes cross a stream on a beaver dam.

Beavers build several types of spillways to take care of the excess water that fills up behind the dam. Often, it is allowed to run over the dam's crest for almost its entire length; at other times it will pour over it at some reinforced point in the crest. Where possible, beavers will prevent water from flowing over the dam by channeling it away at one end so the water flows out harmlessly over solid ground. This is perhaps the safest way, since solid earth can withstand the constant scouring of water much better than the dam.

In times of floods, the pressure on the dam may become so great that it will be washed out. If there is time enough, beavers will usually cut a spillway in the dam itself to relieve the pressure. I have seen this done many times. After the flood waters have subsided, the beavers have only to repair the hole they have cut, which is less work than repairing flood damage to the entire dam.

In an effort to take some of the pressure off the main dam, particularly if it is a long one, the beavers often build subsidiary or reinforcing dams below the main one. These lower dams raise the downstream water up to the base of the main dam and greatly decrease the pressure there. Three or four lower dams built for this purpose may resemble the terraces in the rice paddies of the Philippines. Small dams built upstream from the main one by the beavers increase the accessibility to more food-trees by flooding a greater area.

81

Most of this old
beaver dam has b[...]
washed out by hig[...]
water.

A small secondar[...]
dam supporting t[...]
main dam above[...]

Although almost everything handy is used by beavers in building a dam, by far the oddest material that I ever saw was in a dam in Van Campen's Brook, above my New Jersey home. There was no wood available, and the entire dam was made of cornstalks! This is not an isolated example, however, as I know of its being done on the same stream in the same locality during three different years. The cornstalks did not have the strength of wood, and the dam was easily broached. However, it was the only material available, and the beavers used it. They did not attempt to build a lodge, but lived in holes in the banks of the stream.

All beaver dams are not built alike. Some of them are very sloppy and are the result of the inexperience of the young beavers or the halfhearted efforts of an old bachelor. I have seen several dams that were of such poor construction that the entire mass of material looked as though it had drifted there.

At times, even the most energetic and intelligent beavers cannot cope with the force of the water. Occasionally, families in adjoining colonies may help each other in the repairs to a dam, but usually only one family builds the dam originally. Yet, there are so many reports of young beavers unable to complete their dams and requiring the help of adults that there may be some truth in them. I have heard that these young beavers try repeatedly to dam a stream. When they fail, they are said to seek out an adult whose superior knowledge and experience makes the building of the dam successful. While these stories seem logical, I have no proof they are true. I feel, however, that the beaver story would be incomplete if I did not tell of them.

It is in the building of its dams that the beaver comes into its greatest conflict with man. Often valuable timber is flooded out and water-killed by the beaver ponds, and roads are often inundated or weakened by the rising waters. To a beaver, one of the best spots to build a dam is on a stream above a road or railroad

This dam, just a[ ] miles above the [ ] author's home o[ ] Van Campen's B[ ] is built out of cornstalks.

The author slid[ ] his canoe into t[ ] quiet water abo[ ] an old beaver d[ ]

culvert. The flow of water is already restricted by the steel pipe or concrete culvert that carries it under the highway or railroad. All the beaver needs to do is to build a dam across this narrowed waterway instead of across the full width of the natural stream. There are countless stories and records of the warfare between man and the beaver over its natural instinct to build its dams in such spots. Thousands of dollars and hundreds of man-hours may be spent to oust the beavers. Sometimes the efforts of men are defeated because a challenge of this sort usually brings out the beaver's greatest talents in adapting to the obstacles or in some way circumventing them.

Creosote or oil of tar poured on trees, brush, sticks, the dam itself, or just all over the general area will act as a repellent to beavers, or at least prevent them from picking up the coated sticks in their mouths. However, even this may not deter a really determined beaver. Dams are dynamited, bulldozed, and razed by every means available, and still the beaver fights back. Often, if the beavers would move their dam just a short distance, they would be left in peace. However, it seems that when the beaver once makes up its mind where it wants to build its dam, nothing short of death is going to stop it.

Since beavers are usually protected by state law, outright killing of them because they are a nuisance is forbidden. Under such circumstances the only recourse left is to livetrap them and move them to an area where they are not likely to cause damage. This is not as easy as it might seem because beavers may be wary of traps. Some of them may even spring the trap with a stick and then use the trap as part of the dam.

Much controversy rages about whether a beaver dam is an asset or a detriment to trout fishing. The general opinion today is that most ponds created by the beaver are a help to trout production. It is true that occasionally, in the warmer regions of the country, the water held by the dam warms up so much that the temperature is too high for trout. Another disadvantage for trout is in the removal of trees along the shore of the stream by beavers, which allows more sunlight to strike the water, thus raising its temperature. Also, sediment coming down the stream may settle on the bottom of the pond and cover the gravel beds needed by trout when laying their eggs.

On the other hand, extensive studies have proved that beaver dams are very beneficial to trout. In Wyoming, where the water is too cold to provide adequate food for good trout growth, studies by Grasse and Putnam have proved that the beaver dams were of great benefit to trout. The water of the beaver ponds in these cold streams warmed up enough to allow plentiful hatches of insects on which trout feed, and the growth of the trout was exceptional. The investigators concluded that the beaver ponds were the vital link in trout production. Studies in California also bear this out, and proved that waters dammed up by beavers produced more food and more trout; also, the dams were not a hindrance to the movements of trout, since tagged fish were able to cross the dams at any season.

Besides the advantages to fish, beaver dams and their impounded waters are also a great asset to man. Beaver dams prevent floods by trapping the water high up in the headwaters of streams, preventing it from gaining the momentum that causes destruction. It is far more efficient to dam the smaller tributaries of a stream than to dam the main stream, and the beaver can do the job much better and far cheaper than man. Beaver dams also catch and so reduce the loads of soil sediment that the streams would carry into the manmade dams farther below. Ponds also force more water underground, thus helping low water tables of the land to rise. In addition to providing many wild creatures with an ideal habitat, the ponds also act as storage tanks for livestock in many of the Western streams, as well as providing water for fighting forest fires. Because the water pressure in the streams is reduced by the dams, erosion on lands below them is reduced also.

In order to transport beavers back into the mountainous areas where they can do the most good, many of our states have abandoned the old method of hauling them in by pack horse. Today, beavers are placed in specially designed crates, flown in by airplane, and then parachuted down to the desired spot. Now in a matter of hours the beavers can be put in areas that were once inaccessible, or would have required days of backbreaking work to reach.

One amusing incident involving a beaver dam occurred in the fall of 1962 on the Black River in central New Jersey. Earlier, when beavers moved in, built a dam, and flooded quite a large swamp area, most of the local sportsmen were pleased because of the attractiveness that the pond would have for migrating waterfowl. Everyone looked forward to the hunting season. However, there was a great deal of chagrin on opening day of the duck hunting season when cold weather froze the impounded water, forcing the ducks to go elsewhere.

I have learned to appreciate beaver dams especially when canoeing on some of the smaller streams. Although it requires extra effort for me to get the canoe across the dam, this is more than compensated for by the easy paddling over the long quiet stretch of the pond itself. In fact, ascending some of the swift-running, smaller streams is possible only because of the breaks provided by the quiet waters of beaver ponds.

Fall

MANY SIGNS point conclusively to the coming of colder weather. Each day sees more and more northern ducks drop into the ponds, until at last both the strangers and the residents rise up, circle once for altitude, and move on south. Long wavy *V*'s of geese split the air currents high overhead, and the musical gabble of the flocks comes tumbling down to haunt all who hear it long after their passage. The air has a delightful nip to it that produces crystal days and sparkling nights. The hardwoods are a blaze of riotous color, and their leaves are beginning to tumble down to dapple the surface of the pond, where they are blown about like miniature sailboats by the vagrant breezes. The sensitive ferns have already withered, and the bright orange berries of the mountain ash hang like clusters of bright Japanese lanterns. Fall is in the air, and it drives the beavers into a frenzy of activity.

It is actually the stimulus of the shorter days, or rather the longer nights, that spurs them into redoubled activity. Even captive beavers will attempt to build a lodge for protection against the coming cold weather. Those that have been docile in captivity all summer will now seek escape, if at all possible, with renewed vigor. Although it is said that the beaver will not use its teeth on metal, I have seen them cut holes in a wire pen in the fall. They instinctively know what they need in order to survive the winter, and they do their best to prepare for it. If a beaver ever escapes, it is going to do it at this season.

This large, well-built "island" type of lodge is the peak of beaver construction ability.

This entrance to an auxiliary bank den has been exposed because of a drought.

Fall

At all of the colonies across the land, the dams are checked and reinforced, or raised if more water is needed. Gone are the indolent days of summer. Now every minute counts, and the animals seem to know that it is a race against time and weather.

The lodges have to be built, rebuilt, enlarged, or repaired, according to the circumstances. As each man's home is his castle, so it is with the beaver. In fact, the idea of a moat around a castle may have been taken from the beaver's lodge surrounded by water. The lodge that stands out in the water, completely surrounded like a small island, is the ultimate in evolution of the building of beaver lodges. The earliest and most primitive lodge of the beaver consisted of a burrow in the side of a high bank with the entrance under water. The next step or refinement was the addition of sticks and mud piled over the top of the bank as added protection from predators. The next obvious step was the building of a complete lodge on the top of the bank, but still retaining the underwater entrance. In the final step, the lodge was built up right from the bottom of the pond itself and was completely surrounded by water. This lodge requires the greatest amount of work and ingenuity and offers the greatest amount of protection to the beaver. Many lodges that are on a bank may be molested, but very few of the predators will actually swim out to an island-type lodge.

Some writers have told how a lodge is constructed by beavers laying sticks in a rough circle and building them up like a wall, then roofing it over to complete the lodge. This may happen, but all of the lodges that I have witnessed being built were constructed by the beavers' piling up stick upon stick until they had a goodly mound. Then, coming up underneath the mound, they would cut a room inside of it. Lodges being built out in the water are started by the beavers' anchoring sticks in the mud bottom and just piling up the debris on the top until it protrudes above the water and is

91

The start of a beaver lodge being built over a plunge hole.

Fall

A large beaver lodge on the bank of a small stream.

properly mounded. The same thing is done with a lodge built upon the bank, although here the underwater entrance up to the top of the earth may be completed before the sticks are placed on the top. The beavers do their best to impact the whole mass as tightly as possible. Mud is constantly added to solidify everything. They will also take smaller sticks and work them in between the larger sticks. They will push and tug against the stick until they have shoved it as far as they can into the mass. Then, using their teeth, they cut the stick off flush. Taking the piece of stick that remains, they will again push that in as far as possible and then cut it off. Many of the sticks are cut off after being placed so that no exceptionally long ends protrude.

Mud is dredged up around the lodge and piled up on the sticks. The liquid mud runs down through the sticks like a thin flowing cement and serves the same purposes. The beavers carry the mud in their forepaws or between their chin and forepaws. Usually they have three or four places where they come out of the water onto the lodge. These soon develop into definite runways. When the beaver comes up with a load of mud, it swims up to a runway, then, raising up on its hind legs with its tail dragging for balance, dashes up the roof of the lodge. It goes up till it reaches the desired spot, or until it drops the load or falls, then back it goes for another load. The trips are seemingly endless. More wood is constantly being added while the plastering job is going on, and so the lodge grows. Whether by accident or design, the very peak of the lodge gets practically no mud at all. The peak then serves as a flue or chimney and allows for the ventilation of the chambers inside. The presence of beavers in a colony can easily be discovered by checking the mud on the lodge. If the mud is fresh, the lodge is inhabited: no mud, no beavers. The rains of spring and summer work to wash the mud out from between the sticks, while the beavers constantly add new mud.

Fall

The start of an "island" type beaver lodge.

This lodge being readied for winter is being given a liberal coating of mud.

*Aerial view of a beaver's lodge, showing the "flue" or "chimney" at the
peak. Notice that no mud has been placed there to hamper ventilation.*

A large island-type beaver lodge.

Fall

Even beavers make mistakes. The snow melted by the flood waters shows that this lodge was completely inundated.

The World of the Beaver

Beavers are usually found in any area that has the required water and food. In Glacier National Park, they have been found living right up to the timber line. In some areas of Colorado, they will live in one area in the summer, but may be forced to other locations to find the conditions needed to survive over the winter. One beaver lodge, photographed by A. Radcliffe Dugmore in Newfoundland, was made completely out of mud and roots as there were no trees anywhere in the area. The lack of trees would also force the occupants of the lodge to feed upon the roots of water plants all winter.

A well-constructed lodge is amazingly strong. Some lodges are subject to repeated floodings and come through the submersion with little apparent damage. A bachelor beaver on Van Campen's Brook, in northern New Jersey, in the winter of 1961-62, was constantly being forced out of his lodge by high water. This beaver had built his dam about 600 feet above the junction of the brook with the Delaware River. The dam was solidly built and had backed up a large body of water. However, the dam was no defense against the flooding of the river itself, which forced water up over both the dam and the lodge. The lodge was up on a bank about 3 feet above the dam-controlled water. Each time the river rose, the beaver was forced out of his lodge. This happened on six different occasions and afforded me a wonderful opportunity to take some good beaver photographs in broad daylight. As the rising water melted the snow that blanketed the ground, it left a sharp line of demarcation which gave ample proof that the beaver is not an infallible engineer.

Where possible, beavers will build their lodges on the northern or northwestern part of the pond in order to get the benefit of the greatest amount of sunlight. The extra sunlight will have a tendency to melt the ice away from the lodge itself a little more rapidly, giving the animals greater freedom in the late winter than they would have if the lodge were in another location.

100

View of a beaver house, showing exit holes and center feeding platform.
A flashbulb illuminates the plunge holes (dark spots, center).

An abandoned beaver house that has been cut in half by the author,
showing three plunge holes and the center feeding platform.
The bed was in the foreground on a raised platform. No flashbulb was
used to take this photograph.

Fall

When the young beavers, building their first lodges, are satisfied with their efforts, the chamber inside is then made. I don't mean to say that they wait until the outside of the lodge is completely finished, but they do build the bulk of the lodge first and then cut in from underneath to make the chamber.

There are no sharp bends in the tunnels leading from the underwater entrance to the chambers inside. Later, in winter, branches will have to be brought up these same tunnels to be used as food. If the tunnels were crooked, the branches would get stuck. There are always at least two, and perhaps three, plunge holes or tunnels to each lodge to serve as entrances or escape hatches.

The tunnels come up into a chamber that will vary in size according to the needs of the individual family. The newly paired beavers will have a small chamber perhaps 3 feet in diameter and only 18 inches high. Larger families consisting of the adult male and female, kits, and yearlings will naturally need a larger chamber, and the lodge itself will be much larger. Where the family is very large, there may even be two chambers, or two rooms, in the one lodge, with a dividing wall between them. Each room will have its own entrances.

Each lodge chamber is divided into two sections. The main floor is raised about 4 inches above the water level and serves as a feeding shelf. It also gives the beaver a place to stand to let the water drain from its fur before it climbs onto its bed. The bed, or sleeping shelf, is usually several inches higher, about 6 inches above the water level. The bed will be covered with the soft shredded pieces of wood previously described.

The lodge varies in size with the beaver's needs. A larger family or a long term of occupancy will result in some really good-sized lodges. If a family has adequate food and is not forced to move from the pond or to move to a new location in the pond

103

itself, the lodge will be built larger each fall. As part of the lodge settles, or the chamber needs enlarging, the beavers simply cut a part of the inside wall away until they have the required space.

The largest lodge that I have ever seen is on Lac Landron, in Quebec. It is more than 8 feet high, and the base measures about 40 feet across. This has been occupied continuously for the last five years. A beaver house in Wisconsin measured 14 feet high and 40 feet across.

Samuel Hearne, writing in 1769-72, described a huge lodge in one of the Northeastern states from which the Indians caught thirty-seven beavers at one time, and at that some of the beavers escaped. From other records I am led to believe that this "apartment" type of house was a common feature before the constant pressure was put on the animals by the white man.

John Colter, in 1809, was the first white man to see the wonders of what is now Yellowstone National Park. While there, he escaped from the Blackfoot Indians by diving into the water and entering the tunnel of and hiding in a beaver lodge. Although the lodge was plainly visible to the Indians, it did not occur to them that a man would hide in it.

A few years ago I tried to swim into a beaver lodge built on the headwaters of the Ottawa River in Canada. The lodge itself was in an extensive brushy area, and instead of being built on the edge of the bank, it was hidden deep in the alders, about 25 feet from the water. A drought had exposed the tunnels leading into the lodge, and one of them was large enough to admit the passage of my body. I stripped down and lowered myself into the water. Carl Hartman who was with me waited outside.

The tunnel was about 22 inches in diameter and half filled with water. With a swimming, crawling, sliding motion, I slithered in. There was a slight bend in the tunnel, so that by the time I had gone in about 12 feet, I was in total darkness. As I proceeded, I

The author emerging from the beaver tunnel in which he had been trapped.

The author on a beaver lodge in Quebec that is 33 feet across and 7 feet high.

ran into another difficulty. The roof of the tunnel was becoming lower, which of course made the water higher, and I had to raise my mouth to the top of the tunnel to get air. By the time I could no longer get air, because of the water, I figured I had gone about 18 feet. Not knowing what else lay beyond, I was reluctant to try to make the effort needed to gain the lodge itself. I could feel an enlargement in the tunnel just ahead of me and thought that if I could turn around there, I could then go out headfirst. Taking a last deep breath, I moved forward and did a somersault to turn around. When I was completely upside down, I became wedged between the floor and ceiling, and there I stayed. The only thought that flashed through my mind was, "My God, what a place to get it." With that, I tried to extricate myself. After a great deal of struggling and what seemed to be ages, I was able to upright myself, ending in the same position as when I started. Not caring to make another attempt, I just backed out of the tunnel. I often wondered later just what I would have done if I had made it into the lodge, only to be greeted by a family of angry beavers ready to protect their home. Perhaps it is just as well that I could go no further.

With the dams in good repair and the lodges completed, the beavers next turn their attention to gathering a supply of food to hold them over the frozen winter months. The aspens are by far the most favored beaver food, and they also contain the greatest amount of nutrients. A beaver can smell a freshly cut aspen a long distance and will do everything possible to secure it, a fact that trappers take advantage of. The bark of white, red, and gray birches, maples, willows, alders, poplars, dogwoods, beeches, ashes, cherries, and some oaks are also eaten in the northern United States. Pines, hemlocks, balsams, cedars, spruces, and larches are cut and used for building material but seldom for food. I have only seen one jack pine that was cut and the bark eaten. I have never seen a beaver cut a standing *dead* tree, even for building material.

In the southern parts of the beaver's range, the loblolly pine is the favored food, and they also eat the bark of silver bells, sweet gums, ironwoods, and sweet bays. In Louisiana, where the water does not freeze at all, there is nothing to restrict the beavers' activities in the winter, so they do not bother to store food or make food caches. The southern beavers do not cut down as many trees as their northern cousins either, because they can feed upon other types of vegetation for much longer periods. It has also been found that the southern beavers often eat all the bark off a tree as high as they can reach, and then move on to another without bothering to cut the tree down.

Wildlife research teams have found that a beaver requires 22 to 30 ounces of aspen bark per day for food. Beavers that I have kept in captivity would eat the leaves, bark, and smaller twigs from a 1- to 2-inch-diameter tree every day. To lessen the pressure of these food requirements, I fed them some of the commercial rabbit pellets; they liked them and stayed in good health. The pellets are only a supplementary food. You cannot eliminate the bark of trees from their diets, or the beavers will have trouble when their teeth become too long from lack of chewing.

A tremendous amount of detailed study has been done on the beaver's food requirements by both state and federal wildlife agencies. Most of the studies are concerned with the aspen because the beavers prefer it, it is common throughout most of the United States, and, except where used commercially for pulpwood, it is considered worthless. An aspen tree takes about six to seven years to grow to a 1-inch diameter. At that size, it will produce about 2.85 pounds of food. One acre of 1- to 2-inch-diameter aspens will yield about 5,840 pounds of food, or enough to support ten beavers for one year. As the trees grow larger, instead of sup-

The beaver will often eat all the bark off a wild cherry tree rather than cut into the hard wood. However, this is an excellent example of girdling.

porting more beavers, they will actually support fewer. An acre of 4- to 6-inch-diameter trees will support only seven beavers for one year. This contradiction is based on the fact that the larger the tree, the greater the amount wasted by the beavers. It has been proved that the utilization of 4- to 6-inch-diameter trees is about 36 per cent, with 64 per cent wasted. As the trees gain in diameter, the waste percentage also increases. Many factors contribute to this waste. The beavers will not eat the coarse base bark unless they have to, as they prefer the more tender, succulent twigs. Bigger trees have bigger branches, which may prevent the tree from falling all the way to the ground, so that part of it is out of the beavers' reach. If the tree does fall to the ground, it is much to heavy for the beavers to turn over, so that all the bark on the underside of the tree is wasted. And, after the beavers eat their fill the first night, the larger tree may be abandoned.

When the beavers begin to gather their food supply, they test the trees before they cut them by biting into the bark. If the bark is not in the right condition, or if there is still too much sap in the tree, they may pass the tree by, or they may speed up the conditioning of the tree by girdling it. This dries the bark rapidly. The condition of the bark is very important, because if it is stored underwater before it is ready, it will ferment and sour, rendering it unfit for food.

When the beavers are satisfied that the girdled trees are ready to be cut, usually after five to seven days have passed, they fell them. Trees are now being dropped by the beavers at a tremendous rate. Those closest to the water are cut first because of the ease in handling the material. As the branches are chopped off, the beaver tows them back near the lodge and begins to make its underwater cache. Taking the branch in its teeth, the beaver dives to the bottom and forces the branch into the mud. Most hardwood trees, particularly aspen and birch, are very heavy and have little

Part of a beaver's winter supply of food sticking up above the water.

buoyancy; therefore, beavers have little trouble anchoring them in the mud. More branches are constantly added, so that the additional weight on the top also prevents the bottom branches from moving even if high, fast-running water develops. These food caches are built as close to the lodge as possible to facilitate easy access in the winter when the pond surface is frozen over. Many people mistake the underwater food cache as an unfinished part of the lodge itself.

When the closest trees are all felled, the beavers are forced to go back farther from the water to get their food, and the real labor begins. Pathways are made and become well defined with use. All movable obstructions are cleared; the brush is cut, the grasses eaten, and small staves moved aside. The beavers seem to know that dragging branches and moving logs will be hard enough work without obstacles in the way. It is for this reason that even though the beavers will cut off a hillside, they will not go over the ridge, even if food is plentiful on the other side.

In moving the branches on land, the beaver simply grips the branch in its teeth, turns its head sidewards toward the branch, and walks off, pulling the branch behind him. To move a large branch, the beaver may grasp the butt end in its teeth and back up, pulling the branch along. If the branch is too large, a few quick snips of the beaver's powerful teeth soon cut it to a working size.

To move logs, the animals sometimes pair up, and it is surprising the weight they can move. Logs are seldom pulled on land because the beavers would have no way of towing them. Instead, the logs are rolled, taking advantage of the "wheel" shape of the log itself. They often push the logs with their forefeet, just as you and I would push a log with our hands, or they may roll it by pushing against it with the top of the nose and head. That is why the noses of most beavers are heavily scarred and the hair missing

111

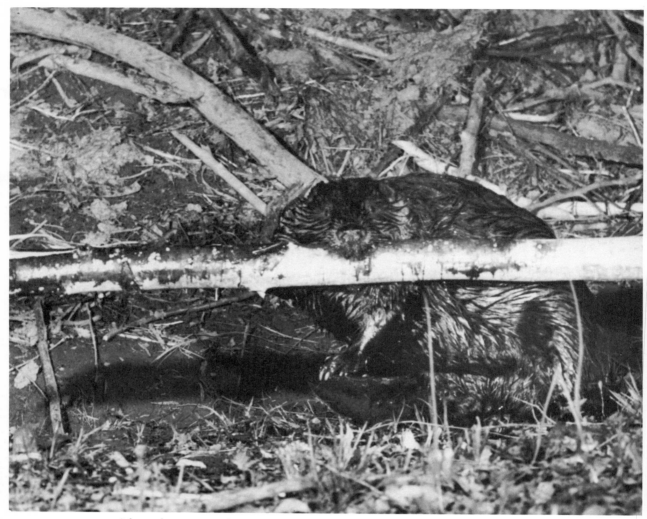

A large beaver carrying an aspen sapling to the water to be used for food.

from the tops of their heads. To move a really heavy log, the beavers place their bodies parallel to the log and push it in the same manner as a human does when pushing with his shoulder, except that beavers use the full lengths of their bodies. Here again, the basic body design of the beaver shows wonderful adaptation. The short legs, compact body, and powerful muscles allow it to get beneath the log and to lift up at the same time that it applies pressure. This will move a round log much faster and easier than will a straight thrust.

Sometimes, if there is a good supply of large trees growing along the water's edge, the beaver will fell an entire tree into the water and not cut the branches off, allowing the ice to seal in everything beneath its surface. In cases like this, the beavers, with seeming economic wisdom, usually eat the bark off the portion of the tree that will be above the ice and will be lost to them in the winter.

There comes a time, however, when the beavers have cut all the available food that can be gathered without too much exposure to danger. In order to stay in their present lodge without being forced to move, they must do one of two things: raise the water level, or build canals.

The raising of the water level is their most common and frequent solution to the problem. Beavers are almost always adding to their dams, so the water is raised quite frequently. One drawback to this method is that the lodge is inundated too. I have seen several lodges that had been abandoned because they were flooded by the beavers' raising the dam height. Not every dam can be raised to obtain the desired results. Dams in narrow canyons or gorges accomplish little with added height. Those located at the head of a meadow or shallow, saucer-like depression can often enlarge the pond to bring hundreds of trees within reach by the addition of a foot or so.

Raising the dam floods a larger area and results in more

Before-and-after photos of a bank lodge as the beavers raised the water to completely surround the lodge.

Fall

water-killed trees. Most people do not begrudge the food-trees eaten by the beavers, but they are hurt financially when beavers kill good standing timber. By actual stump count and by estimating the amount of timber lost in the dead trees, it has been found that in some areas the damage has resulted in the loss of thousands of dollars.

When the desired food-trees cannot be made accessible to them by flooding, the beavers may dig canals to bring water near their standing food supplies. Digging canals is a much more common practice among beavers in the West than among those in the East. A beaver's canals are thought to be the finest examples of its intelligence, ingenuity, and industry.

It can readily be seen that canals can be dug only in fairly flat terrain because they must be dug deep enough to have water in them. For that reason, the longer the canal, the deeper the end away from the pond would have to be to compensate for any grade in the land and give the needed water depth. Most of the canals are dug in an almost straight line, with the beavers depositing the dredged material on either bank. The water depth is usually from twelve to eighteen inches, or just enough to allow the beaver to swim and transport his food. Beavers dig as many canals as they need to make accessible and transportable the necessary food.

On small streams, beavers have been known to build a series of small dams above their main dam to allow them to reach more food, thus forming a series of steps or locks. This practice has also been seen on some of their canals where the beavers have been able to tap or cut into a spring hole or brook to supply the needed water to carry out this project. Beavers fully understand the problem of water levels and their control and have adapted this knowledge to their advantage. They have also been known to divert or to channel springs and streams to the main pond in order to maintain a higher water level.

This small dam was built to back up water among the alders to facilitate the handling of them.

The World of the Beaver

Beavers also dig canals across sections of land to save time and distance. Long spits of land that jut out into lakes or ponds will often have a canal cut across them so that the beaver doesn't have to swim the long way around. If the land is high and a canal would require too much effort, they simply dig a tunnel under it.

Not all of the canals will be visible all of the time because some of them will be underwater a good part of the year and serve as channels of deep water in times of drought. Muskrats will also dig these underwater canals, and during a severe drought, the only water available in the entire pond or marsh may be in them. Even when the water is up to its regular level, the outline of these canals can easily be traced by the darker color of the deeper water. In winter, when the ice has reached a thickness of several feet, beavers can still travel around beneath its surface, even in shallow ponds, by utilizing these canals.

Most of the experience that I have had with canals has been in Quebec, where the countryside is very flat. There the beavers dig the canals primarily to eliminate the distances caused by the streams making oxbows. Most of them are only 40 to 60 feet long and are used as short cuts. There is usually such a profusion of food that long, food-gathering canals are not needed. The longest canal of which I can find a record was 750 feet long and 3 feet deep, a true engineering marvel. It was discovered in 1911 by Enos Mills in the Lily Lake colony near Longs Peak, Colorado.

One other job remains before beavers have finished all possible preparations for the coming winter. They will dig a series of refuge holes at various spots around the lake wherever the bank is high enough to accommodate them. These holes will have underwater entrances, and air chambers that will be above the water level. They are small editions of the bank dens commonly used by some of the beavers as homes, and they give the beavers a spot to rest and breathe in when the pond is covered with ice.

118

A canal leading to a beaver's bank lodge exposed by low water.

They also serve as spots to which the animals retreat if the lodge
is broken into.

At last, with all possible precautions taken, the beavers simply
wait it out as the winter encases their water-world in ice, and the
snowflakes pile up into a blanket that cuts out the light and forces
them to live temporarily in a world of darkness.

Winter

ALTHOUGH the winter imprisons the beavers, it is a lenient jailer, who allows his charges a great deal of leisure time and provides them with a greater measure of protection than any other season. The bitter cold weather, by freezing the pond's surface into ice, creates a means whereby the predators can now walk right out to the lodge. Once there, the predators are held at bay by the same bitter cold that has frozen the mud of the lodge into a concrete consistency rendering the lodge practically impregnable. Late-hibernating bears or an occasional wolverine may chew at the branches, while the froth of frustrated rage splatters on their chests. Their efforts are usually just efforts expended with little chance of reward.

The lodge at this time acts as a magnet to every passing animal. The warmth inside the lodge, created by the beavers' body heat, usually melts the snow from the peak and forms vapors of steam that make it look like a smoking chimney. The track of every predator leads to the lodge where the foxes, the wolves, and the lynxes torment themselves by filling their nostrils with the heady odor of the plump, tasty beavers concealed within. It is a case of so near and yet so far. At last the pangs of hunger set up such a clamor that the predator is forced to turn back to the forest to continue its endless quest for subsistence. This is a part of winter that the beavers know nothing about.

A layer of snow adds to the insulation of the beaver's lodge.

Bears too sometimes catch a beaver on land or try to tear through into the lodge.

Winter

The average beaver family at this time should consist of the two adults, three to four yearlings, and three to four kits. However, many things have taken their toll and reduced the family numbers. There is even one record of a beaver having been killed by an enraged bull moose during the rutting season. Whether the bull had just been defeated in a battle with another amorous bull or whether he killed in the heat of frustration is not known. Whatever the cause, the moose had evidently been looking for some object on which to vent his anger when he came upon the beaver. The beaver's mangled body gave mute testimony to the ferocious attack launched upon him by the huge bull's trampling feet. G. W. Bradt, of Michigan, made extensive studies of fifty-seven colonies of beavers. He found that the wintering populations of the lodges ranged from 1 to 12 beavers, actually averaging out 5.1 beavers per colony.

In addition to predation and accidents, the beaver is subject to various types of diseases and parasites, such as intestinal worms, ringworms, tularemia, pseudotuberculosis, rabies, and lumpy jaw. The fact that each colony tends to stay isolated from other colonies is a big factor in the reduction and prevention of transmission of these ailments. Beavers not only have fewer internal parasites than most other creatures, but they also are plagued less by ectoparasites. Both fleas and lice may be found on them, but are kept to a minimum by the constant use of the combing claws formed by the beaver's split toenails.

The snarling wolverine often tries to capture a beaver by tearing through the roof of the lodge.

123

The World of the Beaver

Milton Stenlund, of the Minnesota Game Division, in 1953 reported one of the largest die-offs of beavers that I can find record of. In the spring of 1952, large numbers of beavers were found dead either in the water or frozen into the ice. Specimens were sent to the Mayo Clinic in Rochester, Minnesota, where the *tularensis* bacterium was identified. In the fall of 1951, hundreds of muskrats and several trappers had contracted tularemia; the beavers had evidently picked up the disease through the water. It was found that those beavers living in ponds were affected much more than were those living in moving water. The disease, although spotty in the areas covered, was widespread, since it was also reported in Ontario and Wisconsin. Most of the beavers had evidently died in the early winter, since the bulk of their food caches had been left untouched. It was estimated that perhaps 25,000 or more had been killed by the disease. Although this is very rare, it has happened before. Back in 1800, a large beaver die-off was reported by John Tanner, who was living in Minnesota with the Indians. He reported that the disease decimated the beavers on impounded waters and that they never came back to their peak numbers.

The beavers might have caught tularemia directly from the muskrats because they are in almost constant contact with them. In some cases, muskrats have been known to move into the lodge with the beavers.

On two different occasions, I have surprised muskrats sunning themselves on the outside of a beaver's lodge. Alarmed, the muskrats dived into the water and did not reappear. There was no other cover nearby, but I cannot prove the muskrats sought refuge in the lodge itself, although I believe they did. The beaver is a fairly sociable fellow and probably wouldn't object to having a muskrat in its lodge.

The fact that the beaver family all stays together in the one

124

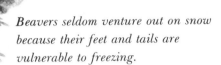

Beavers seldom venture out on snow because their feet and tails are vulnerable to freezing.

lodge is of great importance to them, because warm-blooded animals can stay warmer in a group than if they live singly. Not only can they huddle together for actual contact body warmth, but a large number of them in confined quarters give off enough heat to raise the temperature considerably.

The deep water around the lodge and the underwater entrance to the lodge now become doubly important to the beavers. Although the surface of the pond is frozen solid, the deep underwater entrance allows them unrestricted passage. Very rarely, a drought or a broken dam will cause the water level to drop, allowing the underwater passage to freeze solid too. When this happens, beavers are forced to eat a part of the lodge for subsistence. If the condition is of long duration, the beavers may die of starvation.

Ordinarily the beaver experiences no such difficulty. The cold water does not bother him, protected as he is by his body fat and waterproof fur. Many people fail to realize that although the air may be bitter cold and the temperature 50 degrees below zero, the water that the beaver is swimming in is still warmer than 32 degrees, or it wouldn't be water, it would be ice. Further proof that the beaver is relatively unaffected by the cold is the length of time that it takes a beaver's pelt to become fully developed, or "prime." Land animals such as the fox, raccoon, and skunk, or any of the others that brave the cold weather, have prime coats by November or December. The coats of the water animals such as the muskrat and beaver do not fully develop until February and

125

The World of the Beaver

March. The beaver molts but once a year, shedding his long winter coat in the late spring or summer. The condition of the fur is best seen from the flesh side of the hide. When the fur is unprime or not fully developed, the black roots of each individual hair will be seen on the flesh side of the pelt. This gives a "blue" appearance. When the fur is prime and the hair has grown out fully, the root hairs can no longer be seen, and the flesh side will be a creamy white in color. Naturally, the pelts or hides that are fully developed when the animals are killed are of the greatest value, which is why beaver trapping is almost always carried on in late winter.

When a beaver wants food in the wintertime, he takes a deep breath, slides into the water, swims out the underwater passage, and dives down to get a branch from the food cache. In working underwater, the beaver's fur mouth flaps effectively seal off the oral passages, and the beaver can chew and cut the wood and not get either water or chips in his mouth. Returning to the lodge with a branch, the beaver sits on the feeding shelf and starts to feed. The branch is usually cut into short lengths of about a foot in order to facilitate handling. The beaver sits upright and turns the stick with his forepaws, chewing off the bark with a "corn on the cob" technique. Branches chewed by beavers have a circular "threaded" appearance like a machine bolt. When all the bark is removed, the stick is discarded out in the open water. These sticks may be retrieved at a later date and used in the construction or repair of the lodge or dam. The beaver makes as many trips to the food cache as is necessary to satisfy his hunger.

Quite frequently, the beaver will dig up the roots of whatever water plants are available to give him a change of diet. The gathering of roots and branches from the food cache does not put too great a strain on the beaver's supply of oxygen, because both activities are carried on comparatively close to the lodge. Occasionally, however, an extended trip under the ice may be made requiring more than one breath of air. Breathing under the ice is no great problem to the beaver either.

The water level will often drop after the pond freezes, allowing a pocket of air to form under the ice. If the blanket of air does not extend under the entire surface of the ice, there are always numerous pockets of it. Anyone who has ever walked or skated on ice is familiar with the white air pockets that show where the water is not in contact with the ice. These air pockets give the beavers a source of oxygen and allow them to travel about under the ice almost at will.

If, for some reason, the beaver cannot find an air pocket when he needs it, he can simply exhale the air in his lungs and then swim up to the ice, where the same breath of air will be trapped, and breathe it in again. The filtering action of the water seems to remove some of the carbon dioxide and renews the oxygen. While other have witnessed beavers doing this, I have not, although I did see a muskrat doing it. If something should scare the beaver away from its air bubble before it can be breathed in, the beaver, of course, will die. He must have oxygen.

The beavers probably have their greatest weight in the wintertime because of their stored body fat and their comparative inactivity. Age of a beaver is more accurately told by weight than by any other means once the animal is past the kit stage. Grasse and Putnam, in their Wyoming beaver studies, have formed the following age estimates based upon the actual weighing of hundreds of beavers. The kits weigh from 9 to 15 pounds the first winter, the yearlings 24 pounds, the two-year-olds 29 pounds, and adults from 40 pounds on up. No one yet has come up with a yardstick for accurate aging.

Breeding takes place in January or February, depending upon the area the beaver inhabits. The southern beavers naturally mate earlier than do those of the Far North. The experts are divided upon the question of whether the beaver is monogamous or polygamous. I believe monogamy is not so much a matter of choice as of conditions. The beaver's world at this time is restricted to the actual pond in which its lodge is located. Although the male may seek out additional females if given the choice, the ice conditions eliminate the matter of choice.

Occasionally a small male may lose out to a larger male, but there is no evidence of beavers establishing the harems that other animals do. That jealousy does exist among beavers is shown by the fact that strange males entering a colony will usually be attacked by the presiding male of that colony. Strange females will be attacked by the adult resident female.

Futher proof of monogamy is that tagged beaver mates that have been livetrapped will usually remain as a pair till death takes one from the other. The beavers are really good examples of all that we hold to be honorable as mates and parents.

Copulation takes place in the water, where it can help support the beaver's body weight. The dorsoventral position common to most animals is employed by the beavers. Reports of beaver copulating ventrally are usually sightings of the beavers playing or wrestling. Records of the copulation of beavers are made with captive specimens because the ice prevents the act being seen in the wilds.

The peaceful existence of the beavers is usually shattered in February when the trapping season, where allowed, is usually opened. The beaver is not difficult to trap. The greatest adversary that the trapper has to face is the weather. The snow and ice that protect the beavers against most of their enemies give them small protection from the trappers. Various types of sets are made, but most of them employ a device to cause the beaver to drown. Traps are seldom set or allowed to be set in the actual entrances to the lodge. These entrances are usually in water too deep for the

This toe was undoubtedly lost to a trap.

trapper to reach. The most common set is made by fastening the trap on a shelf of sticks nailed to a pole. The trap is then baited with fresh aspen sticks, and the entire pole is thrust through a hole in the ice. In trying to reach the fresh food, the beaver is caught and quickly drowned in the deep water.

Traps placed in shallow water, on the dam or other spot where the beaver does not drown, may cause a wring-off. A beaver caught where he cannot drown will usually twist around and around in the trap until his foot is torn off. This usually happens when the beaver is caught by his forefoot. The hind foot, being larger and stronger, does not usually allow this to happen. Sometimes a beaver will be caught in a small trap and lose just a toe or two. Beavers have been known to live in apparently good condition with the loss of three of their legs. To prevent undue suffering, no trapper should ever set a trap that does not immediately drown his catch.

The male is usually the first beaver caught, since he is the one to investigate the disturbance created by the trapper cutting through the ice. The female follows and so on till the colony is wiped out. Discerning trappers set their traps at a distance from the lodge to prevent the capture of the kits, who are not prone to swim as far under the ice. This is a good conservation practice, because it insures a supply of beavers being left for breeding purposes.

The World of the Beaver

Occasionally, a beaver will become trap wise and will spring the trap with a stick, or else stay away from it entirely. If the trapper disturbs the lodge too much, the entire family may leave it and move into their refuge holes in the bank.

The Indians have developed a beaver dog called a "Squeewan." As pointers and setters are trained to locate game birds, beaver dogs are trained to locate beavers. That they can do this even though there are several feet of ice and snow on top of the water has been demonstrated countless times. In using a beaver dog, the Indians will pound on the lodge with a club. The frightened beavers inside vacate the lodge and seek out their refuge holes. The dog then runs across the ice, following the beaver swimming beneath, and locates the entrance to the refuge hole. Although the entrance to the lodge is usually in water too deep to place a trap, this is not the case with the bank holes. The Indians then cut a hole in the ice and place a trap in the entrance to the refuge hole, which practically guarantees their catching the beaver when he comes back out.

And so the cycle of the beaver is completed. Those that have escaped death in its many forms eagerly await and accept the challenge that is a part of each new spring. They know not what problems will be presented, but they are confident that they can meet and overcome them with the talents and abilities endowed them by the Creator.

Beavers and Men

THE WORD "beaver" is taken from the old Anglo-Saxon word "beofor" and the word "castor" comes from the Greek. The earliest writings about beavers were done in Egyptian hieroglyphics, and the early Greek historians mention the beaver several times.

The Castoroides, or early beaver of the Pleistocene era, was a monster weighing about 700 pounds. From that period of one million years ago, the beaver has shrunk in size and range. Our present-day type of beaver was found throughout all of Europe, except Ireland, in most of Asia, as far south as the Euphrates River, and over most of the North American continent. Florida, the fringe of the Gulf region, and the desert areas of the United States have never had a beaver population in historical times.

The beaver's industry has always been admired by man, and with good reason. The beaver has figured prominently in folklore, legend, and history. Many of our American Indian tribes trace their beginnings back to the beaver. According to a Cherokee Indian legend, it was the Great Spirit, with the help of gigantic beavers, who created the earth. The earth had been covered with water until the Great Spirit sent the beavers diving down beneath the surface to dredge up mud from the bottom to form the land masses. The beavers of lore built up the earth much as the beavers of today build up their lodges.

131

The World of the Beaver

Beavers and Men

The Crow Indians venerated the beavers because they believed that when they died they would come back to this earth in the form of a beaver. Consequently, they believed that each beaver was the reincarnation of some Indian, probably a relative or friend.

The Flathead Indians didn't hold the beavers in such high esteem because they believed that the beavers were a race of Indians that had fallen from favor with the Great Spirit and had been changed into the form of beavers. The industry of the beavers was to atone for their sins and was to be abolished after the beavers had labored long enough. When this time came, the beavers were again to be elevated to the status of men.

The various Indian words for beaver are very similar. In the Algonquin tongue, the word for beaver is *amik,* the Cree word is *amisk,* and the Chippewa word is *ahmik.* An old Algonquin friend of mine, Charlie Smith of Maniwaki, Quebec, gave me the following descriptive words for the beaver. A male beaver is called *nabeamik,* a female is *noceamik,* a big beaver of either sex is a *kitciamik,* while a little one is an *amikons.* The Algonquin word for beaver castor is *amik wicina.*

It was the skins of the beavers that brought the Indians and the white men into greatest contact and conflict. The trade for beaver pelts started on the very first day that the Pilgrims stepped ashore in the New World. They were greeted by the Indian Samoset, who wore beaver skins as a part of his clothing. The furs caught the eyes of the Pilgrims, and they, through sign language, conveyed the idea to Samoset that they wanted to trade for the furs and that he should return with more of them.

Ernest Thompson Seton has estimated that at the time of the coming of the white man, there were at least sixty million beavers in the area that we now call the United States. Every stream, pond, and lake that had available food supported its colony of beavers. The beaver was, and is to this day, used as much for food as for

133

fur by the Indians, who hunted them all year. The beaver, more than any other factor, was responsible for the early exploration of our country.

The Dutch settled along the Hudson River, the English along the New England coast, and the French along the St. Lawrence River. The conflicts and the resultant wars between these peoples and their nations were fought not so much for the territory that each occupied as for the control of the very lucrative fur trade of the respective regions. Albany, New York, became the world's leading port for the shipment of furs. In 1763, Pierre Laclede and August Chouteau founded a fur trading post at the junction of the Missouri and Mississippi rivers. This post grew rapidly and became known at St. Louis. By the mid-1800's this city had become the raw fur center of the whole world, but most of the fur still was transshipped through Albany.

On May 2, 1670, the Hudson's Bay Company came into existence for the express purpose of trading with the Indians for fur. Beaver pelts were, of course, the main items of trade. By utilizing Hudson Bay, James Bay, and their tributary rivers, the heartland of the continent was opened to exploration and development before all of the Eastern seacoast was fully settled. The French got along better with the Indians than the English did, because the French embraced the Indian way of life and were content to be hunters, trappers, and traders. The English were more interested in cutting down the forests and opening up the way for permanent settlements.

Many fur companies were formed over the years, and many fortunes were made. In addition to the Hudson's Bay Company, the American Fur Company, the Northwest Company, the Columbia Fur Company, the Pacific Fur Company, the Rocky Mountain Fur Company, and the St. Louis, Missouri Fur Company are all well known and played an important part in our nation's history. In a single year, several hundred thousand beaver pelts would be traded by these companies. The Hudson's Bay Company alone traded in over three million beaver pelts in the years from 1853 to 1877. The companies not only traded for the pelts with the Indians, they also sent large groups of their own trappers out into the mountains to take the furs in direct competition with the Indians. Individual trappers, known as the "mountain men," also pursued the beavers wherever they could be found.

The "rendezvous," or annual gathering of trappers in one location to sell their pelts to the traders, grew to be of tremendous importance to the fur trade. Here the trappers would bring their pelts to sell or exchange them for guns, powder, lead, foodstuffs, and liquor. This week-long trading festival would allow the trappers to sell their furs without making the even longer trip to the fur centers. Old friends would be seen and adventures related. As death by accident or at the hands of Indians was always a very good possibility, the mountain men worked hard and played hard.

The invention of the steel trap by Sewell Newhouse at Oneida, New York, in 1823 allowed the trappers to take tremendous numbers of beavers much more easily. James Pattie, trapping in Arizona on the San Francisco River in 1825, caught 250 beavers in just two weeks' time. Alexander Ross, with a company of twenty trappers, trapped in the Bitterroot Mountains between the Missouri and Columbia rivers in 1824. His records show that 95 beavers were taken in one morning and 60 more throughout the day, making a total of 155 beavers in one day. The entire season was very successful, and they caught more than 5,000 beavers, not counting other types of animals. Beavers were so numerous in South Dakota in 1874 that General George Custer's expedition against the Sioux was handicapped by the numerous flooded areas.

Beaver pelts at that time were sold by the pound. A large pelt would weigh between 1 to 2 pounds and the price was four dollars per pound. Eighty skins would make a 100-pound pack and be valued at three to five hundred dollars in the mountains. On the average, a trapper could expect to take three beavers a day throughout the season. This made his daily take about sixteen dollars. Back east a man working on a farm could expect to get fifty cents per day and his meals. So it is easy to see why any man with a little adventure in his heart would head for the hills to trap beavers. Nothing was really easy about trapping the beaver except the catching of the animal. The traps were heavy, each weighing about 5 pounds, and cost from twelve to sixteen dollars apiece. In addition, the trapper had to fight off Indians, wild animals, disease, bitter cold, deep snows, and loneliness. The solitary trapper might go months without seeing another person; yet he had to be constantly on guard against danger.

The competition between the trapper and the Indian, between trapper and trapper, and between the rival companies became so fierce that bloodshed and all sorts of cutthroat tactics were resorted to. The main losers, of course, were the beavers. They were trapped so constantly and pursued so relentlessly that they were almost eliminated entirely.

The most common use of the beaver pelts was in the manufacture of beaver hats. The fur was combed with a special comb that removed most of the fine underhair, leaving the guard hairs intact. This underfur was then wetted down and kneaded into a felt, which was then made into a high hat. Every man who could afford a hat just had to have one made of beaver. The discovery in 1840 that silk could be used for this purpose gave the beaver some relief from trapping as the price of their pelts crashed downward. Today most of the large beaver pelts are sheared, resulting in a soft luxurious fur that does not have the weight and the bulk of the original fur.

Two other interesting items concerning the old-time beaver

trapping and trade are the standards that the Hudson's Bay Company established for the related value of their blankets and guns to beaver pelts. A point system was set up for the blankets whereby the 3-, 3½-, and 4-point blankets were valued at or could be exchanged for 3 large, 3 large and 1 small, and 4 large beaver pelts respectively. A common misbelief is that the old-time muzzle-loading guns had such long barrels in order to increase their value in beaver pelts. It is said that the rifle would be stood on end and beaver pelts would be piled up until they made a stack as high as the gun. This would have made these guns extremely costly. Actual tests have proved that it would require anywhere from 250 to 400 beaver skins to make a stack 4½ to 5½ feet high, or to reach the muzzles of the old guns. The guns had the long barrels in order to get the maximum gas pressure from the slow-burning black powder. Even so, although it sometimes cut down the accuracy of the gun, the Indians used to saw off some of the barrel length to facilitate handling the gun in heavy cover or on horseback.

Actually, the Hudson's Bay Company had an established value for each of the various types of guns, which differed from post to post only because of the distances involved in getting the guns to the posts for trade. The value of a gun ranged from eight to fourteen beaver pelts. Four to five pounds of lead could be purchased for one beaver pelt, and a single pelt would also buy about 1½ pounds of black powder.

These figures are based on what is known, in the trade, as a "blanket" beaver pelt. Beaver pelts are stretched round or oval in shape while being dried. To determine the size of the pelt, the two diameters of width and length are added together. A pelt thus measured that scales more than 70 inches is considered a large-size or "blanket" pelt.

The constant and relentless trapping of the beavers completely wiped them out over most of their natural range. The cutting down of the forests and the opening up of the country also speeded their extirpation. The beavers were wiped out of the northeastern portion of the country at an early date because it had the largest human population. By 1820, the last beaver was gone from New Jersey. New Hampshire had some in Coos County till about 1865. Pennsylvania's beavers were gone by 1890, and most of New York was also devoid of beavers by that time. Later research showed that a few beavers had managed to survive in the most remote areas of the Adirondacks, but for all practical purposes New York beavers were considered depleted. The situation was the same throughout the entire country. Since the beavers were very scarce, there was no law protecting them, so that when a colony was discovered, the inhabitants were promptly killed.

Canadian beavers fared no better than their American counterparts. Even back in the wilderness, beavers could not be found. Whole tribes of Indians were poverty-stricken when their main source of revenue was wiped out.

It was only in the last decade of the 1800's that enough people became concerned over the beavers' plight to force some action to save the remnants. State after state passed laws giving the beavers complete protection.

The closing of the seasons was a last-ditch fight for the survival of the species. Many people felt that the beaver, like the bison, had served its purpose and was on its way out. They felt that the need for beavers was over. The general sentiment was that "it was too bad about the loss of the beaver, but that was the way it worked out." We can be thankful that there were enough interested people to attempt the restocking of beavers needed to reestablish them. States, such as Wisconsin, Wyoming, Minnesota, and Michigan, that were fortunate enough to have some beavers left in the wilds were generous enough to share their meager stocks with their less fortunate sister states.

A beaver caught in a Bailey live trap.

Joseph Taylor, New Jersey state trapper, removing a nuisance beaver for transplanting.

Beavers and Men

New Jersey's first reestablished wild beavers escaped from the Rutherford Stuyvesant estate in 1900 and founded colonies in Sussex County. The following year, 1901, beavers reappeared in Monroe County, Pennsylvania, directly across the Delaware River from Sussex County, New Jersey. It is thought that these beavers were also from the Stuyvesant stock. New York State imported six beavers in 1904 and estimated that there were perhaps twelve beavers left of the original stock in the Adirondacks. Pennsylvania stocked beavers from Wisconsin in 1917. Virginia stocked beavers in 1915, and West Virginia in 1922. Washington, Oregon, and California noticed an increase in their beaver numbers about this time, and so it goes. Given the needed protection and the restocking where they had been eliminated, the pendulum for the beaver started to swing the other way.

As is so often the case with pendulums, this one swung too far. By the 1920's the beavers had so successfully reestablished themselves that the nuisance complaints began to pour in. Many of the complaints were legitimate, caused by the beavers' flooding out valuable timber, stopping up drainage ditches, spoiling irrigation ditches, and wreaking all kinds of havoc. In other instances, the complaints were fostered by greed. The fur price boom of the 1920's was on, and the prices paid for beaver pelts skyrocketed. Forty to fifty dollars was a common price for a pelt and a record of one hundred dollars for one pelt was set by the London Fur Sale.

The beaver problem became a real thorn in the side of the various conservation departments. Population studies, census counts, habitat investigations, and life history studies were undertaken by most of the states, and a wealth of factual material was poured out. There is probably more written work of this kind on the beaver than on any other species of animal.

At first, most of the states handled the nuisance beavers by

141

having conservation department men livetrap the offenders and transplant them to areas where they could be safely released. The situation finally got out of hand as an ever-growing clamor was set up. On one side of the issue were the trappers, lumbermen, and farmers who wanted to trap the beavers either for monetary gains or for relief from their depredations. On the other side were the resort area owners, conservationists, and the general public, who liked the beavers, liked to see the beavers, and who realized the good done by the beavers.

A great many beavers were trapped illegally, and the skins were transported to areas where trapping was legal. Law enforcement agencies had a tremendous job enforcing the laws over such widespread wilderness areas.

At last, when the data were in and evaluated, most of the states began to experiment with open trapping seasons. Length of seasons, the time of the seasons, area permits, limitation of numbers trapped, tagging of pelts, and many other methods of control were tried. It was found that 30 to 35 per cent of the total beaver population could be taken each year without depleting the brood stock or affecting the beaver population's stability. Most of the trapping seasons today are based upon an annual census of the beavers' numbers. Whereas in former days this census was carried out laboriously by men on foot or in a canoe, today the airplane is used. The use of the airplane for censusing is not only quicker, it is actually cheaper. Most of the censuses are taken in the fall, because at that time the beavers have built their food caches. There may be several lodges on a single pond, but only those lodges that have a food cache are counted. It is basic knowledge that a beaver family builds only one food cache, and that cache is as close to the lodge as possible. Furthermore, the cache is of such a size that it is easily seen from the air. Many people, Indians included, used to judge the severity of the forthcoming winter by

A beaver's bank lodge and his cache of food for winter.

Meadow created by an ancient beaver dam.

the size of the beavers' food cache. A large cache meant a hard winter, a small cache was supposed to mean a short winter. There is no basis for these conclusions. If anything, the opposite is probably closer to the truth. An easy or late-arriving winter will allow the beavers more time to gather food, so the cache will actually be larger, since they add to it until the pond freezes over.

Today, most of the states are cognizant of the many facets of beaver management and intelligently handle the individual problems of a local nature for the greatest benefit of the majority of the people. Livetrapping operations, using the Bailey trap, allow the states to secure breeding stock to be planted on the headwaters of streams, where the dams and ponds effectively control silt and prevent flooding and erosion. Regulated trapping seasons allow the over-all population to be kept within the limits of the food supply, prevent excessive damage, and provide a cash income for the trappers. Since World War II, when pelt values reached a high of seventy-five dollars, the prices have declined to a low of six dollars and are now bringing an average of about twelve dollars. Still, the total value of beavers trapped each year runs into the hundreds of thousands of dollars, which is an amount large enough to warrant wise management of this natural resource.

Beaver farming has been tried from time to time, but most of these attempts have failed because of the low price of the fur compared to the amount of labor and expense involved. Some breeders have tried small holding-pens, while others have fenced in good-sized areas. The closest approach to practical farming of beavers is the wise management of large wilderness areas that have suitable habitats for beaver culture.

Beaver workings are probably second only to the workings of man in the changing of the ecology of a region. When the beavers move into a new area, almost all related factors undergo a radical change. Many of the smaller creatures which may have inhabited

145

the flood plain, such as the voles and shrews, will be flooded out and forced up to higher ground or out of the area entirely. Musk-rats that may not have lived along the fast-moving stream will certainly move into the retained water of the pond. Mink and otters will stay at the pond longer because the water now occupies a greater area, and there will undoubtedly be a great many more fish. Trout may or may not be favored, according to the water temperature, but there will be more fish of some species. Moose and deer that may have been feeding on the willows, alders, and maples on the banks of the stream will have to forego these trees as the beavers utilize them. As a replacement, there will be more water plants such as the eelgrass and lilies to tempt the herbivores. Both the deer and the moose will seek relief in the deeper waters of the pond to escape the hordes of mosquitoes that hatch out in the shallows. Many creatures will find the pond itself an obstacle to their travels over land; yet the dam will serve as a bridge over the stream. The water-killed trees will serve as a home for tree swal-lows, and the woodpeckers will find in them a home and happy hunting ground. The hawks and owls will find their hunting range reduced as the voles are forced to retreat; yet the heron's range will be extended, since it can feed upon minnows and tadpoles of the pond. Every pond will be host to at least one family of ducks, and in most cases three or four families, sometimes of two or three different species.

As the beavers continue to work, they bring about many steps of plant succession that sometimes work to their own detriment. Quite frequently, when the beavers fell the aspens, growing on the higher land surrounding the pond, the additional sunlight that reaches the understory will allow the climatic cover, such as the firs, to shoot upward. As the firs mature, they will keep out the aspens, reducing the amount of beaver food. Here, then, is an instance of the beavers working against themselves.

This view of a beaver walking away shows the characteristic shoesole type of tail.

The World of the Beaver

The darker, or "cedar," water of a pond will prevent the rapid growth of water plants that clear water would allow, and this too is an important feature in food production. A pond may silt up with rich topsoil, or the fill may be very acid and poor.

After the tenure of the beavers is over and the dam begins to decay, these two soil factors will govern the type of plant life that will grow again in the area and the length of time it will take the plants to return. The good topsoil will result in a rich meadowland that will support a luxurious growth of all types of vegetation. In a situation like this, it does not take too long for the various steps in plant succession to occur. In the poor, acid soil, the growth will be very slow, and it will take years of cleansing rains to wash out the undesirable elements from it. In any event, the beaver very definitely leaves his mark upon the land.

A beaver is a beaver is a beaver. That is, except to the taxonomists, who find that there are *twenty-five* living subspecies of the genus Castor in North America. The differences between the subspecies are in size, color, and range. The darker-furred animals are the more desirable from a commercial viewpoint and are the ones favored by most of the game commissions as breeding stock. Today, it is all but impossible to differentiate between the subspecies because of the tremendous inadvertent crossbreeding done by man. With the beavers all but wiped out by the 1900's, man had to get replacement stock where he could. The introduced subspecies are now found in ranges where they had never been found before, and they have also crossbred with whatever wild native stock was available.

List of Beaver Subspecies

The following list of beaver subspecies and their ranges has been taken from the *List of North American Recent Mammals,* by Gerrit S. Miller, Jr. and Remington Kellogg, United States National Museum Bulletin 205, 1955.

1.   *Castor canadensis canadensis* is considered the typical beaver type. It inhabits most of the wooded regions from Hudson Bay to British Columbia, to the Yukon, and south to Wyoming.

2.   *Castor canadensis caecator.* The Newfoundland beaver is found only on the Island of Newfoundland.

3.   *Castor canadensis michiganensis.* The Woods beaver of Michigan, Minnesota, Wisconsin, and Ontario is one of the darkest-colored beavers and one of the most valuable.

4.   *Castor canadensis labradorensis.* The Labrador beaver is found only in eastern Labrador on rivers draining into the Atlantic Ocean.

5.   *Castor canadensis acadicus.* The Acadian beaver, the beaver of New England in colonial times, is found in New Brunswick, Nova Scotia, parts of Quebec, and south to the Adirondacks in New York.

6.   *Castor canadensis carolinensis.* The Carolina beaver ranged from New Jersey south through the Carolinas to Georgia and west to Louisiana and Mississippi.

149

7. *Castor canadensis texensis.* The Texas beaver inhabited the eastern and northern portions of that state.

8. *Castor canadensis missouriensis.* The Missouri River beaver is found in the drainage of the Missouri River in Kansas, North and South Dakota, Iowa, Montana, Saskatchewan, and Alberta.

9. *Castor canadensis concisor.* The Colorado beaver is found in the elevated mountainous sections of that state and northeastern New Mexico.

10. *Castor canadensis duchesnei.* The Duchesne River beaver is found in the Duchesne and White rivers of Utah and Colorado.

11. *Castor canadensis pallidus.* The Raft River beaver is found only in the Raft River Mountains of Utah.

12. *Castor canadensis rostralis.* The Utah beaver is found in the western-flowing streams of the Wasatch Mountains.

13. *Castor canadensis mexicanus.* The Mexican beaver inhabits all of the Rio Grande basin of Texas and New Mexico.

14. *Castor canadensis frondator.* The Sonoran beaver is found in western New Mexico and Sonora, Mexico.

15. *Castor canadensis repentinus.* The Grand Canyon beaver inhabits Nevada, Arizona, California, Colorado, and Utah in the drainage areas of the Colorado River.

16. *Castor canadensis subauratus.* The golden beaver was so named because of the color of its fur. It is found in the San Joaquin, Kings, and Sacramento rivers.

17. *Castor canadensis shastensis.* The Shasta beaver is from the northeastern part of California and Oregon.

18. *Castor canadensis baileyi.* The Nevada beaver comes from the Humboldt River in Nevada and the Blitzen and Silvies rivers in Oregon.

19. *Castor canadensis taylori.* The Idaho beaver is found in the Snake River drainage of that state and possibly in western Utah.

20. *Castor canadensis pacificus.* The Washington beaver is found

in Washington, northern Oregon, northern Idaho, and the southern portion of British Columbia.

21. *Castor canadensis idoneus.* The Oregon beaver is found along the coastal area of Oregon and Washington and Puget Island.

22. *Castor canadensis leucondontus.* The Pacific beaver is found only on Vancouver Island in British Columbia.

23. *Castor canadensis sagittatus.* The British Columbian beaver is found in the interior of that province north to the Yukon, and south into northern Idaho.

24. *Castor canadensis belugae.* The Cook's Inlet beaver is found in the Cook Inlet of Alaska as well as in Stikine River and the Bella Coola River.

25. *Castor canadensis phaeus.* The Admiralty Island beaver is found only on the island whose name it bears.

My thoughts often stray to the Indian legend of how the Creator had to call upon the great beavers to help build the earth. It is reassuring to see the beavers coming back so strongly over almost all of their range. As intent as man seems to be on destroying the earth, the Creator may again have to call upon the beavers to help patch things up. The earth's future couldn't be in better paws.

Bibliography

ANTHONY, H. E. *Animals of America*. Garden City, N.Y.: Garden City Publishing Co., 1937.

BAILEY, VERNON. *Wild Animals of Glacier National Park*. Washington, D.C.: Government Printing Office, 1918.

————. *Beaver Habits and Experiments in Beaver Culture*. Technical Bulletin 31, United States Department of Agriculture, Government Printing Office, 1927.

BENNITT, RUDOLPH, and NAGEL, WERNER O. *Survey of Furbearers of Missouri*. Columbia, Mo.: University of Missouri, 1937.

BOURLIÈRE, FRANÇOIS. *The Natural History of Mammals*. New York: Alfred A. Knopf, 1954.

————. *Mammals of the World*. New York: Alfred A. Knopf, 1955.

BRONSON, WILFRID S. *The Chisel-tooth Tribe*. New York: Harcourt, Brace & Co., 1939.

BURNS, EUGENE. *The Sex Life of Wild Animals*. New York: Rinehart & Co., Inc., 1953.

CAHALANE, VICTOR H. *Mammals of North America*. New York: The Macmillan Co., 1947.

CHITTENDEN, HIRAM MARTIN. *American Fur Trade of the Far West*. Stanford, Calif.: Academic Reprints, 1954.

CORY, CHARLES B. *The Mammals of Illinois and Wisconsin*. Chicago: Field Museum of Natural History, 1912.

COUCH, LEO K. *Trapping and Transplanting Live Beavers*. Washington, D.C.: Government Printing Office, 1942.

152

Bibliography

DEVOE, ALAN. *This Fascinating Animal World.* New York: McGraw-Hill Book Co., Inc., 1951.

DRIMMER, FREDERICK. *Illustrated Encyclopedia of Animal Life.* New York: Greystone Press, 1960.

GRIMM, WILLIAM C., and ROBERTS, HARVEY A. *Mammal Survey of Pennsylvania.* Harrisburg, Pa.: Pennsylvania Game Commission, 1950.

GRASSE, JAMES E., and PUTNAM, ERIVERN F. *Mammal Survey of Pennsylvania.* Harrisburg, Pa.: Pennsylvania Game Commission, 1950.

GUNDERSON, HARVEY L., and BEER, JAMES R. *The Mammals of Minnesota.* Minneapolis, Minn.: University of Minnesota Press, 1953.

HAMILTON, WILLIAM J., JR. *American Mammals.* New York: McGraw-Hill Book Co., Inc., 1939.

_____.*The Mammals of Eastern United States.* Ithaca, N.Y.: Comstock Publishing Co., Inc., 1943.

HANDLEY, CHARLES O., JR., and PATTON, CLYDE P. *Wild Mammals of Virginia.* Richmond, Va.: Commission of Game and Inland Fisheries, 1947.

HODGDON, KENNETH W., and HUNT, JOHN H. *Beaver Management in Maine.* Augusta, Me.: Department of Inland Fisheries and Game, 1953.

JACKSON, HARTLEY H. T. *Mammals of Wisconsin.* Madison, Wisc.: University of Wisconsin Press, 1961.

JOHNSON, CHARLES EUGENE. "The Beaver in the Adirondacks: Its Economics and Natural History." *Roosevelt Wild Life Bulletin,* Vol. 3, No. 4, Syracuse University, 1927.

The Journal of Mammalogy. All articles on beavers in issues from 1926-62.

The Journal of Wildlife Management. All articles on beavers in issues from 1937-62.

LEIGHTON, ROGER S., and LEE, JAMES A. *A Technique to Control Water Levels in Beaver Impoundments.* Concord, N.H.: New Hampshire Fish and Game Department.

LONG, WILLIAM J. *The Spirit of the Wild.* Garden City, N.Y.: Doubleday & Co., Inc., 1956.

Bibliography

McSPADDEN, J. WALKER. *Animals of the World.* Garden City, N.Y.: Garden City Publishing Co., Inc., 1942.

MILLS, ENOS A. *In Beaver World.* Boston and New York: Houghton Mifflin Co., 1913.

MOORE, CLIFFORD B. *Ways of Mammals.* New York: The Ronald Press Co., 1953.

MOORE, GEORGE C., and MARTIN, ERNEST C. *Status of Beaver in Alabama.* Montgomery, Ala.: Department of Conservation, 1949.

NELSON, E. W. *Wild Animals of North America.* Washington, D.C.: The National Geographic Society, 1930.

PIETSCH, LYSLE R. *The Beaver In Illinois.* Urbana, Ill.: Department of Conservation and Illinois Natural History Survey, 1956.

SANDERSON, IVAN T. *Living Mammals of the World.* Garden City, N.Y.: Hanover House, 1956.

SCHWARTZ, CHARLES W. and ELIZABETH R. *The Wild Mammals of Missouri.* Columbia, Mo.: University of Missouri Press, 1959.

SETON, ERNEST THOMPSON. *Lives of Game Animals.* Boston: Charles T. Branford Co., 1953.

SHIRAS, GEORGE, 3RD. *Hunting Wild Life with Camera and Flashlight.* Washington, D.C.: National Geographic Society, 1935.

SILVER, HELENETTE. *History of New Hampshire Game and Furbearers.* Concord, N.H.: New Hampshire Fish and Game Department, 1957.

SMITH, KENNETH C. *Beaver in Louisiana.* Louisiana Wild Life and Fisheries Commission.

STONE, WITMER, and CRAM, WILLIAM E. *American Animals.* New York: Doubleday, Page & Co., 1902.

TAPPE, DONALD T. *The Status of Beaver in California.* Sacramento, Calif.: California State Printing Office, 1942.

TAYLOR, WALTER P. *The Status of the Beavers of Western North America.* Berkeley, Calif.: University of California Press, 1916.

———, and SHAW, WILLIAM T. *Mammals and Birds of Mt. Rainier National Park.* Washington, D.C.: Government Printing Office, 1927.

Bibliography

TEVIS, LLOYD, JR. *Summer Behavior of a Family of Beavers in New York State.* Reprint from *Journal of Mammalogy,* 1950.

TRIPPENSSE, REUBEN E. *Wildlife Management.* New York: McGraw-Hill Book Co., Inc., 1953.

WARREN, EDWARD R. "The Beaver in Yellowstone National Park." *Roosevelt Wild Life Annals,* Vol. 1, Nos. 1 and 2, Syracuse University, 1926.

Index

157

The World of the Beaver

11223

#11003